W9-ADW-143

THE TEMPTATION

OF

ST. ANTONY

OR,

A REVELATION OF THE SOUL

BY

GUSTAVE FLAUBERT

VOLUME VII.

SIMON P. MAGEE,
PUBLISHER,
CHICAGO, ILL.

CONTENTS

THE TEMPTATION OF ST. ANTONY

OVER STRAND AND FIELD

(vii)

CONTENTS

ILLUSTRATIONS

TEMPTATION OF SAINT ANTONY

OVER STRAND AND FIELD

THE

Temptation *of* Saint Antony

CHAPTER I.

A Holy Saint.

T IS in the Thebaïd, on the heights of a mountain, where a platform, shaped like a crescent, is surrounded by huge stones.

The Hermit's cell occupies the background. It is built of mud and reeds, flat-roofed and doorless. Inside are seen a pitcher and a loaf of black bread; in the centre, on a wooden support, a large book; on the ground, here and there, bits of rush-work, a mat or two, a basket and a knife.

Some ten paces or so from the cell a tall cross is planted in the ground; and, at the other end of the platform, a gnarled old palm-tree leans over the abyss, for the side of the mountain is scarped; and at the bottom of the cliff the Nile swells, as it were, into a lake.

To right and left, the view is bounded by the enclosing rocks; but, on the side of the desert, immense undulations of a yellowish ash-colour rise, one above and one beyond the other, like the lines of a seacoast; while, far off, beyond the sands, the mountains of the Libyan range form a wall of chalk-like whiteness faintly shaded with violet haze. In front, the sun is going down. Towards the north, the sky has a pearl-grey tint; while, at the zenith, purple clouds, like the tufts of a gigantic mane, stretch over the blue vault. These purple streaks grow browner; the patches of blue assume the paleness of mother-of-pearl. The bushes, the pebbles, the earth, now wear the hard colour of bronze, and through space floats a golden dust so fine that it is scarcely distinguishable from the vibrations of light.

Saint Antony, who has a long beard, unshorn locks, and a tunic of goatskin, is seated, cross-legged, engaged in making mats. No sooner has the sun disappeared than he heaves a deep sigh, and gazing towards the horizon:

"Another day! Another day gone! I was not so miserable in former times as I am now! Before the night was over, I used to begin my prayers; than I would go down to the river to fetch water, and would reascend the rough mountain pathway, singing a hymn, with the water-bottle on my shoulder. After that, I used to amuse myself by arranging everything in my cell. I used to take up my tools, and examine the mats, to see whether they were evenly cut, and the baskets, to see whether they were light; for it seemed to me then that even my most trifling acts were duties which I performed with ease. At regulated hours I left off my work and prayed, with my two arms extended. I felt as if a fountain of mercy were flowing from Heaven above into my heart. But now it is dried up. Why is this? . . ."

He proceeds slowly into the rocky enclosure.

"When I left home, everyone found fault with me. My mother sank into a dying state; my sister, from a distance, made signs to me to come back; and the other one wept. Ammonaria, that child whom I used to meet every evening, beside the cistern, as she was leading away her cattle. She ran after me. The rings on her feet glittered in the dust, and her tunic, open at the hips, fluttered in the wind. The old ascetic who hurried me from the spot addressed her, as we fled, in loud and menacing tones. Then our two camels kept galloping continuously, till at length every familiar object had vanished from my sight.

"At first, I selected for my abode the tomb of one of the Pharaohs. But some enchantment surrounds those subterranean palaces, amid whose gloom the air is stifled with the decayed odour of aromatics. From the depths of the sarcophagi I heard a mournful voice arise, that called me by name — or rather, as it seemed to me, all the fearful pictures on the walls started into hideous life. Then I fled to the borders of the Red Sea into a citadel in ruins. There I had for companions the scorpions that crawled amongst the stones, and, overhead, the eagles who were continually whirling across the azure sky. At night, I was torn by talons, bitten by beaks, or brushed with light wings; and horrible demons, yelling in my ears, hurled me to the earth. At last, the drivers of a caravan, which was journeying towards Alexandria, rescued me, and carried me along with them.

"After this, I became a pupil of the venerable Didymus. Though he was blind, no one equalled him in knowledge of the Scriptures. When our lesson was ended, he used to take my arm, and, with my aid, ascend the Panium, from whose summit could be seen the Pharos and the open sea. Then we would return home, passing along the quays, where we brushed against men of every nation, including the Cimmerians, clad in bearskin, and the Gymnosophists of the Ganges, who smear their bodies with cow-dung. There were continual conflicts in the streets, some of which were caused by the Jews' refusal to pay taxes, and others by the attempts of the seditious to drive out the Romans. Besides, the city is filled with heretics, the followers of Manes, of Valentinus, of Basilides, and of Arius, all of them eagerly striving to discuss with you points of doctrine and to convert you to their views.

"Their discourses sometimes come back to my memory; and, though I try not to dwell upon them, they haunt my thoughts.

"I next took refuge in Colzin, and, when I had undergone a severe penance, I no longer feared the wrath of God. Many persons gathered around me, offering to become anchorites. I imposed on them a rule of life in antagonism to the vagaries of Gnosticism and the sophistries of the philosophers. Communications now reached me from every quarter, and people came a great distance to see me.

"Meanwhile, the populace continued to torture the confessors; and I was led back to Alexandria by an ardent thirst for martyrdom. I found on my arrival that the persecution had ceased three days before. Just as I was returning, my path was blocked by a great crowd in front of the Temple of Serapis. I was told that the Governor was about to make one final example. In the centre of the portico, in the broad light of day, a naked woman was fastened to a pillar, while two soldiers were scourging her. At each stroke her entire frame writhed. Suddenly, she cast a wild look around, her trembling lips parted; and, above the heads of the multitude, her figure wrapped, as it were, in her flowing hair, methought I recognised Ammonaria. . . . Yet this one was taller— and beautiful, exceedingly!"

He draws his hand across his brow.

"No! no! I must not think upon it!

"On another occasion, Athanasius asked me to assist him against the Arians. At that time, they had confined themselves to attacking him with invectives and ridicule. Since then, however, he has been calumniated, deprived of his see, and banished. Where is he now? I know not! People concern themselves so little about bringing me any news! All my disciples have abandoned me, Hilarion like the rest.

"He was, perhaps, fifteen years of age when he came to me, and his mind was so much filled with curiosity that every moment he was asking me questions. Then he would listen with a pensive air; and, without a murmur, he would run to fetch whatever I wanted—more nimble than a kid, and gay enough, moreover, to make even a patriarch laugh. He was a son to me!"

The sky is red; the earth completely dark. Agitated by the wind, clouds of sand rise, like winding-sheets, and then fall again. All at once, in a clear space in the heavens, a flock of birds flits by, forming a kind of triangular battalion, resembling a piece of metal with its edges alone vibrating.

Antony glances at them.

"Ah! how I should like to follow them! How often, too, have I not wistfully gazed at the long boats with their sails resembling wings, especially when they bore away those who had been my guests! What happy times I used to have with them! What outpourings! None of them interested me more than Ammon. He described to me his journey to Rome, the Catacombs, the Coliseum, the piety of illustrious women, and a thousand other things. And yet I was unwilling to go away with him! How came I to be so obstinate in clinging to this solitary life? It might have been better for me had I stayed with the monks of Nitria when they besought me to do so. They occupy separate cells, and yet communicate with one another. On Sunday the trumpet calls them to the church, where you may see three whips hung up, which are reserved for the punishment of thieves and intruders, for they maintain very severe discipline.

"Nevertheless, they do not stand in need of gifts, for the faithful bring them eggs, fruit, and even instruments for removing thorns from their feet. There are vineyards around Pisperi, and those of Pabenum have a raft, in which they go forth to seek provisions.

"But I should have served my brethren more effectually by being a simple priest. I might succour the poor, administer the sacraments, and guard the purity of domestic life. Besides, all the laity are not lost, and there was nothing to prevent me from being, for example, a grammarian or a philosopher. I should have had in my room a sphere made of reeds, tablets always in my hand, young people around me, and a crown of laurel suspended as an emblem over my door.

"But there is too much pride in such triumphs! Better be a soldier. I was strong and courageous enough to manage engines of war, to traverse gloomy forests, or, with helmet on head, to enter smoking cities. More than this, there would be nothing to hinder me from purchasing with my earnings the office of toll-keeper of some bridge, and travellers would relate to me their histories, pointing out to me heaps of curious objects which they had stowed away in their baggage.

"On festival days the merchants of Alexandria sail along the Canopic branch of the Nile and drink wine from cups of lotus, to the sound of tambourines, which make all the taverns near the river shake. Beyond, trees, cut cone-fashion, protect the peaceful farmsteads against the south wind. The roof of each house rests on slender columns running close to one another, like the framework of a lattice, and, through these spaces, the owner, stretched on a long seat, can gaze out upon his grounds and watch his servants thrashing corn or gathering in the vintage, and the cattle trampling on the straw. His children play along the grass; his wife bends forward to kiss him."

Through the deepening shadows of the night pointed snouts reveal themselves here and there with ears erect and glittering eyes. Antony advances towards them. Scattering the wind in their wild rush, the animals take flight. It was a troop of jackals.

One of them remains behind, and, resting on two paws, with his body bent and his head on one side, he places himself in an attitude of defiance.

"How pretty he looks! I should like to pass my hand softly over his back."

Antony whistles to make him come near. The jackal disappears.

"Ah! he is gone to join his fellows. Oh! this solitude! this weariness!"

Laughing bitterly:

"This is such a delightful life — to twist palm branches in the fire to make shepherds' crooks, to turn out baskets and fasten mats together, and then to exchange all this handiwork with the Nomads for bread that breaks your teeth! Ah! wretched me! will there never be an end of this? But, indeed, death would be better! I can bear it no longer! Enough! Enough!"

He stamps his foot, and makes his way through the rocks with rapid step, then stops, out of breath, bursts into sobs, and flings himself upon the ground.

The night is calm; millions of stars are trembling in the sky. No sound is heard save the chattering of the tarantula.

The two arms of the cross cast a shadow on the sand. Antony, who is weeping, perceives it.

"Am I so weak, my God? Courage! Let us arise!"

He enters his cell, finds there the embers of a fire, lights a torch, and places it on the wooden stand, so as to illumine the big book.

"Suppose I take — the 'Acts of the Apostles' — yes, no matter where!

"'He saw the sky opened with a great linen sheet which was let down by its four corners, wherein were all kinds of terrestrial animals and wild beasts, reptiles and birds. And a voice said to him: Arise, Peter! Kill and eat!'

"So, then, the Lord wished that His apostle should eat every kind of food? . . . whilst I . . ."

Antony lets his chin sink on his breast. The rustling of the pages, which the wind scatters, causes him to lift his head, and he reads:

"'*The Jews slew all their enemies with swords, and made a great carnage of them, so that they disposed at will of those whom they hated.*'

"There follows the enumeration of the people slain by them — seventy-five thousand. They had endured so much! Besides, their enemies were the enemies of the true God. And how they must have enjoyed their vengeance, completely slaughtering the idolaters! No doubt the city was gorged with the dead! They must have been at the garden gates, on the staircases, and packed so closely together in the various rooms that the doors could not be closed! But here am I plunging into thoughts of murder and bloodshed!"

He opens the book at another passage.

"'*Nebuchadnezzar prostrated himself with his face on the ground and adored Daniel.*'

"Ah! that is good! The Most High exalts His prophets above kings. This monarch spent his life in feasting, always intoxicated with sensuality and pride. But God, to punish him, changed him into a beast, and he walked on four paws!"

Antony begins to laugh; and, while stretching out his arms, disarranges the leaves of the book with the tips of his fingers. Then his eyes fall on these words:

"'*Ezechias felt great joy in coming to them. He showed them his perfumes, his gold and silver, all his aromatics, his sweet-smelling oils, all his precious vases, and the things that were in his treasures.*'

"I can imagine how they beheld, heaped up to the very ceiling, gems, diamonds, darics. A man who possesses such an accumulation of these things is not the same as others. While handling them, he assumes that he holds the result of innumerable exertions, and that he has absorbed, and can again diffuse, the very life of the people. This is a useful precaution for kings. The wisest of them all was not wanting in it. His fleets brought him ivory — and apes. Where is this? It is——"

He rapidly turns over the leaves.

"Ah! this is the place:

"' *The Queen of Sheba, being aware of the glory of Solomon, came to tempt him, propounding enigmas.*'

"How did she hope to tempt him? The Devil was very desirous to tempt Jesus. But Jesus triumphed because He was God, and Solomon owing, perhaps, to his magical science. It is sublime, this science; for — as a philosopher has explained to me — the world forms a whole, all whose parts have an influence on one another, like the different organs of a single body. It is interesting to understand the affinities and antipathies implanted in everything by Nature, and then to put them into play. In this way one might be able to modify laws that appear to be unchangeable."

At this point the two shadows traced behind him by the arms of the cross project themselves in front of him. They form, as it were, two great horns. Antony exclaims:

"Help, my God!"

The shadows resume their former position.

"Ah! it was an illusion — nothing more. It is useless for me to torment my soul. I have no need to do so — absolutely no need!"

He sits down and crosses his arms.

"And yet methought I felt the approach . . .
But why should *he* come? Besides, do I not know
his artifices? I have repelled the monstrous anchorite who, with a laugh, offered me little hot loaves;
the centaur who tried to take me on his back; and
that vision of a beautiful dusky maid amid the sands,
which revealed itself to me as the spirit of voluptuousness."

Antony walks up and down rapidly.

"It is by my direction that all these holy retreats
have been built, full of monks wearing hair-cloths
beneath their goatskins, and numerous enough to
furnish forth an army. I have healed diseases at a
distance. I have banished demons. I have waded
through the river in the midst of crocodiles. The
Emperor Constantine has written me three letters;
and Balacius, who treated with contempt the letter I
sent him, has been torn by his own horses. The
people of Alexandria, whenever I reappeared amongst
them, fought to get a glimpse of me; and Athanasius
was my guide when I took my departure. But what
toils, too, I have had to undergo! Here, for more
than thirty years, have I been constantly groaning in
the desert! I have carried on my loins eighty pounds
of bronze, like Eusebius; I have exposed my body to
the stings of insects, like Macarius; I have remained
fifty-three nights without closing an eye, like Pacho-
mius; and those who are decapitated, torn with
pincers, or burnt, possess less virtue, perhaps, inasmuch as my life is a continual martyrdom!"

Antony slackens his pace.

"Certainly there is no one who undergoes so
much mortification. Charitable hearts are growing
fewer, and people never give me anything now. My

cloak is worn out, and I have no sandals, nor even a porringer; for I gave all my goods and chattels to the poor and my own family, without keeping a single obolus for myself. Should I not need a little money to get the tools that are indispensable for my work? Oh! not much—a little sum! . . . I would husband it.

"The Fathers of Nicæa were ranged in purple robes on thrones along the wall, like the Magi; and they were entertained at a banquet, while honours were heaped upon them, especially on Paphnutius, merely because he has lost an eye and is lame since Dioclesian's persecution! Many a time the Emperor has kissed his injured eye. What folly! Moreover, the Council had such worthless members! Theophilus, a bishop of Scythia; John, another, in Persia; Spiridion, a cattle-drover. Alexander was too old. Athanasius ought to have made himself more agreeable to the Arians in order to get concessions from them!

"How is it they dealt with me? They would not even give me a hearing! He who spoke against me —a tall young man with a curling beard—coolly launched out captious objections; and while I was trying to find words to reply to him, they kept looking at me with malignant glances, barking at me like hyenas. Ah! if I could only get them all sent into exile by the Emperor, or rather smite them, crush them, behold them suffering. I have much to suffer myself!"

He sinks swooning against the wall of his cell.

"This is what it is to have fasted overmuch! My strength is going. If I had eaten, only once, a morsel of meat!"

He half-closes his eyes languidly.

"Ah! for some red flesh . . . a bunch of grapes to nibble, some curds that would quiver on a plate!

"But what ails me now? What ails me now? I feel my heart dilating like the sea when it swells before the storm. An overwhelming weakness bows me down, and the warm atmosphere seems to waft towards me the odour of hair. Still, there is no trace of a woman here."

He turns towards the little pathway amid the rocks.

"This is the way they come, poised in their litters on the black arms of eunuchs. They descend, and, joining together their hands, laden with rings, they kneel down. They tell me their troubles. The need of a superhuman voluptuousness tortures them. They would like to die; in their dreams they have seen gods who called them by name; and the edges of their robes fall round my feet. I repel them. 'Oh! no,' they say to me, 'not yet! What must I do?' Any penance will appear easy to them. They ask me for the most severe: to share in my own, to live with me.

"It is a long time now since I have seen any of them! Perhaps, though, this is what is about to happen? And why not? If suddenly I were to hear the mule-bells ringing in the mountains. It seems to me . . ."

Antony climbs upon a rock, at the entrance of the path, and bends forward, darting his eyes into the darkness.

"Yes! down there, at the very end, there is a moving mass, like people who are trying to pick their way. Here it is! They are making a mistake."

Calling out:

"On this side! Come! Come!"

The echo repeats:

"Come! Come!"

He lets his arms fall down, quite dazed.

"What a shame! Ah! poor Antony!"

And immediately he hears a whisper:

"Poor Antony."

"Is that anyone? Answer!"

It is the wind passing through the spaces between the rocks that causes these intonations, and in their confused sonorities he distinguishes voices, as if the air were speaking. They are low and insinuating, a kind of sibilant utterance:

The first—"Do you wish for women?"

The second—"Nay; rather great piles of money."

The third—"A shining sword."

The others—"All the people admire you."

"Go to sleep."

"You will cut their throats. Yes! you will cut their throats."

At the same time, visible objects undergo a transformation. On the edge of the cliff, the old palm-tree, with its cluster of yellow leaves, becomes the torso of a woman leaning over the abyss, and poised by her mass of hair.

Antony re-enters his cell, and the stool which sustains the big book, with its pages filled with black letters, seems to him a bush covered with swallows.

"Without doubt, it is the torch that is making this play of light. Let us put it out!"

He puts it out, and finds himself in profound darkness.

And, suddenly, through the midst of the air, passes first, a pool of water, then a prostitute, the corner of a temple, a figure of a soldier, and a chariot with two white horses prancing.

These images make their appearance abruptly, in successive shocks, standing out from the darkness like pictures of scarlet above a background of ebony.

Their motion becomes more rapid; they pass in a dizzy fashion. At other times they stop, and, growing pale by degrees, dissolve — or, rather, they fly away, and instantly others arrive in their stead.

Antony droops his eyelids.

They multiply, surround, besiege him. An unspeakable terror seizes hold of him, and he no longer has any sensation but that of a burning contraction in the epigastrium. In spite of the confusion of his brain, he is conscious of a tremendous silence which separates him from all the world. He tries to speak; impossible! It is as if the link that bound him to existence was snapped; and, making no further resistance, Antony falls upon the mat.

CHAPTER II.

HEN, a great shadow — more sub-
tle than an ordinary shadow, from
whose borders other shadows hang
in festoons — traces itself upon the
ground.

It is the Devil, resting against the
roof of the cell and carrying under his wings — like a
gigantic bat that is suckling its young — the Seven
Deadly Sins, whose grinning heads disclose themselves
confusedly.

Antony, his eyes still closed, remains languidly
passive, and stretches his limbs upon the mat, which
seems to him to grow softer every moment, until it
swells out and becomes a bed; then the bed becomes
a shallop, with water rippling against its sides.

To right and left rise up two necks of black soil
that tower above the cultivated plains, with a sycamore here and there. A noise of bells, drums, and
singers resounds at a distance. These are caused by
people who are going down from Canopus to sleep
at the Temple of Serapis. Antony is aware of this,
and he glides, driven by the wind, between the two
banks of the canal. The leaves of the papyrus and
the red blossoms of the water-lilies, larger than a

man, bend over him. He lies extended at the bottom of the vessel. An oar from behind drags through the water. From time to time rises a hot breath of air that shakes the thin reeds. The murmur of the tiny waves grows fainter. A drowsiness takes possession of him. He dreams that he is an Egyptian Solitary.

Then he starts up all of a sudden.

"Have I been dreaming? It was so pleasant that I doubted its reality. My tongue is burning! I am thirsty!"

He enters his cell and searches about everywhere at random.

"The ground is wet! Has it been raining? Stop! Scraps of food! My pitcher broken! But the water-bottle?"

He finds it.

"Empty, completely empty! In order to get down to the river, I should need three hours at least, and the night is so dark I could not see well enough to find my way there. My entrails are writhing. Where is the bread?"

After searching for some time he picks up a crust smaller than an egg.

"How is this? The jackals must have taken it, curse them!"

And he flings the bread furiously upon the ground.

This movement is scarcely completed when a table presents itself to view, covered with all kinds of dainties. The table-cloth of byssus, striated like the fillets of sphinxes, seems to unfold itself in luminous undulations. Upon it there are enormous quarters of flesh-meat, huge fishes, birds with their feathers, quadrupeds with their hair, fruits with an almost natural colouring; and pieces of white ice and flagons of violet crystal shed glowing reflections. In the middle of the table Antony observes a wild boar smoking from all its pores, its paws beneath its belly, its eyes half-closed — and the idea of being able to eat this formidable animal rejoices his heart exceedingly. Then, there are things he had never seen before — black hashes, jellies of the colour of gold, ragoûts, in which mushrooms float like water-lilies on the surface of a pool, whipped creams, so light that they resemble clouds.

And the aroma of all this brings to him the odour of the ocean, the coolness of fountains, the mighty perfume of woods. He dilates his nostrils as much as possible; he drivels, saying to himself that there is enough there to last for a year, for ten years, for his whole life!

In proportion as he fixes his wide-opened eyes upon the dishes, others accumulate, forming a pyramid, whose angles turn downwards. The wines begin to flow, the fishes to palpitate; the blood in the dishes bubbles up; the pulp of the fruits draws nearer, like amorous lips; and the table rises to his breast, to his very chin — with only one seat and one cover, which are exactly in front of him.

He is about to seize the loaf of bread. Other loaves make their appearance.

"For me! . . . all! but——"

Antony draws back.

"In the place of the one which was there, here are others! It is a miracle, then, exactly like that the Lord performed! . . . With what object? Nay, all the rest of it is not less incomprehensible! Ah! demon, begone! begone!"

He gives a kick to the table. It disappears.

"Nothing more? No!"

He draws a long breath.

"Ah! the temptation was strong. But what an escape I have had!"

He raises up his head, and stumbles against an object which emits a sound.

"What can this be?"

Antony stoops down.

"Hold! A cup! Some one must have lost it while travelling—nothing extraordinary!——"

He wets his finger and rubs.

"It glitters! Precious metal! However, I cannot distinguish——"

He lights his torch and examines the cup.

"It is made of silver, adorned with ovolos at its rim, with a medal at the bottom."

He makes the medal resound with a touch of his finger-nail.

"It is a piece of money which is worth from seven to eight drachmas—not more. No matter! I can easily with that sum get myself a sheepskin."

The torch's reflection lights up the cup.

"It is not possible! Gold! yes, all gold!"

He finds another piece, larger than the first, at the bottom, and, underneath that many others.

"Why, here's a sum large enough to buy three cows—a little field!"

The cup is now filled with gold pieces.

"Come, then! a hundred slaves, soldiers, a heap wherewith to buy——"

Here the granulations of the cup's rim, detaching themselves, form a pearl necklace.

"With this jewel here, one might even win the Emperor's wife!"

With a shake Antony makes the necklace slip over his wrist. He holds the cup in his left hand, and with his right arm raises the torch to shed more light upon it. Like water trickling down from a basin, it pours itself out in continuous waves, so as to make a hillock on the sand — diamonds, carbuncles, and sapphires mingled with huge pieces of gold bearing the effigies of kings.

"What? What? Staters, shekels, darics, aryandics! Alexander, Demetrius, the Ptolemies, Cæsar! But each of them had not as much! Nothing impossible in it! More to come! And those rays which dazzle me! Ah! my heart overflows! How good this is! Yes! . . . Yes! . . . more! Never enough! It did not matter even if I kept flinging it into the sea; more would remain. Why lose any of it? I will keep it all, without telling anyone about it. I will dig myself a chamber in the rock, the interior of which will be lined with strips of bronze; and thither will I come to feel the piles of gold sinking under my heels. I will plunge my arms into it as if into sacks of corn. I would like to anoint my face with it — to sleep on top of it!"

He lets go the torch in order to embrace the heap, and falls to the ground on his breast. He gets up again. The place is perfectly empty!

"What have I done? If I died during that brief space of time, the result would have been Hell — irrevocable Hell!"

A shudder runs through his frame.

"So, then, I am accursed? Ah! no, this is all my own fault! I let myself be caught in every trap. There is no one more idiotic or more infamous. I would like to beat myself, or, rather, to tear myself

out of my body. I have restrained myself too long.
I need to avenge myself, to strike, to kill! It is as if
I had a troop of wild beasts in my soul. I would
like, with a stroke of a hatchet in the midst of a
crowd—— Ah! a dagger! . . ."

He flings himself upon his knife, which he has
just seen. The knife slips from his hand, and Antony
remains propped against the wall of his cell, his
mouth wide open, motionless—like one in a trance.

All the surroundings have disappeared.

He finds himself in Alexandria on the Panium—
an artificial mound raised in the centre of the city,
with corkscrew stairs on the outside.

In front of it stretches Lake Mareotis, with the
sea to the right and the open plain to the left, and,
directly under his eyes, an irregular succession of flat
roofs, traversed from north to south and from east
to west by two streets, which cross each other, and
which form, in their entire length, a row of porticoes
with Corinthian capitals. The houses overhanging
this double colonnade have stained-glass windows.
Some have enormous wooden cages outside of them,
in which the air from without is swallowed up.

Monuments in various styles of architecture are
piled close to one another. Egyptian pylons rise
above Greek temples. Obelisks exhibit themselves
like spears between battlements of red brick. In the
centres of squares there are statues of Hermes with
pointed ears, and of Anubis with dogs' heads. Antony
notices the mosaics in the court-yards, and the tapestries hung from the cross-beams of the ceiling.

With a single glance he takes in the two ports
(the Grand Port and the Eunostus), both round like
two circles, and separated by a mole joining Alexan-

dria to the rocky island, on which stands the tower of the Pharos, quadrangular, five hundred cubits high and in nine storys, with a heap of black charcoal flaming on its summit.

Small ports nearer to the shore intersect the principal ports. The mole is terminated at each end by a bridge built on marble columns fixed in the sea. Vessels pass beneath, and pleasure-boats inlaid with ivory, gondolas covered with awnings, triremes and biremes, all kinds of shipping, move up and down or remain at anchor along the quays.

Around the Grand Port there is an uninterrupted succession of Royal structures: the palace of the Ptolemies, the Museum, the Posideion, the Cæsarium, the Timonium where Mark Antony took refuge, and the Soma which contains the tomb of Alexander; while at the other extremity of the city, close to the Eunostus, might be seen glass, perfume, and paper factories.

Itinerant vendors, porters, and ass-drivers rush to and fro, jostling against one another. Here and there a priest of Osiris with a panther's skin on his shoulders, a Roman soldier, or a group of negroes, may be observed. Women stop in front of stalls where artisans are at work, and the grinding of chariot-wheels frightens away some birds who are picking up from the ground the sweepings of the shambles and the remnants of fish. Over the uniformity of white houses the plan of the streets casts, as it were, a black network. The markets, filled with herbage, exhibit green bouquets, the drying-sheds of the dyers, plates of colours, and the gold ornaments on the pediments of temples, luminous points — all this contained within the oval enclosure of the greyish walls, under the vault of the blue heavens, hard by the motionless sea.

But the crowd stops and looks towards the eastern side, from which enormous whirlwinds of dust are advancing.

It is the monks of the Thebaïd who are coming, clad in goats' skins, armed with clubs, and howling forth a canticle of war and of religion with this refrain:

"Where are they? Where are they?"

Antony comprehends that they have come to kill the Arians.

All at once, the streets are deserted, and one sees no longer anything but running feet.

And now the Solitaries are in the city. Their formidable cudgels, studded with nails, whirl around like monstrances of steel. One can hear the crash of things being broken in the houses. Intervals of silence follow, and then the loud cries burst forth again. From one end of the streets to the other there is a continuous eddying of people in a state of terror. Several are armed with pikes. Sometimes two groups meet and form into one; and this multitude, after rushing along the pavements, separates, and those composing it proceed to knock one another down. But the men with long hair always reappear.

Thin wreaths of smoke escape from the corners of buildings. The leaves of the doors burst asunder; the skirts of the walls fall in; the architraves topple over.

Antony meets all his enemies one after another. He recognises people whom he had forgotten. Before killing them, he outrages them. He rips them open, cuts their throats, knocks them down, drags the old men by their beards, runs over children, and beats those who are wounded. People revenge themselves on luxury. Those who cannot read, tear the books to pieces; others smash and destroy the statues, the paintings, the furniture, the cabinets — a thousand dainty objects whose use they are ignorant of, and which, for that very reason, exasperate them. From time to time they stop, out of breath, and then begin again. The inhabitants, taking refuge in the court-yards, utter lamentations. The women lift their eyes to Heaven, weeping, with their arms bare. In order to move the Solitaries they embrace their knees; but the latter only dash them aside, and the blood gushes up to the ceiling, falls back on the linen clothes that line the walls, streams from the trunks of decapitated corpses, fills the aqueducts, and rolls in great red pools along the ground.

Antony is steeped in it up to his middle. He steps into it, sucks it up with his lips, and quivers with joy at feeling it on his limbs and under his hair, which is quite wet with it.

The night falls. The terrible clamour abates.

The Solitaries have disappeared.

Suddenly, on the outer galleries lining the nine stages of the Pharos, Antony perceives thick black lines, as if a flock of crows had alighted there. He hastens thither, and soon finds himself on the summit.

A huge copper mirror turned towards the sea reflects the ships in the offing.

Antony amuses himself by looking at them; and as he continues looking at them, their number increases.

They are gathered in a gulf formed like a crescent. Behind, upon a promontory, stretches a new city built in the Roman style of architecture, with cupolas of stone, conical roofs, marble work in red and blue, and a profusion of bronze attached to the volutes of capitals, to the tops of houses, and to the angles of cornices. A wood, formed of cypress-trees, overhangs it. The colour of the sea is greener; the air is colder. On the mountains at the horizon there is snow.

Antony is about to pursue his way when a man accosts him, and says:

"Come! they are waiting for you!"

He traverses a forum, enters a court-yard, stoops under a gate, and he arrives before the front of the palace, adorned with a group in wax representing the Emperor Constantine hurling the dragon to the earth. A porphyry basin supports in its centre a golden conch filled with pistachio-nuts. His guide informs him that he may take some of them. He does so.

Then he loses himself, as it were, in a succession of apartments.

Along the walls may be seen, in mosaic, generals offering conquered cities to the Emperor on the palms of their hands. And on every side are columns of basalt, gratings of silver filigree, seats of ivory, and tapestries embroidered with pearls. The light falls from the vaulted roof, and Antony proceeds on his way. Tepid exhalations spread around; occasionally he hears the modest patter of a sandal. Posted in the ante-chambers, the custodians — who resemble automatons — bear on their shoulders vermilion-coloured truncheons.

At last, he finds himself in the lower part of a hall with hyacinth curtains at its extreme end. They divide, and reveal the Emperor seated upon a throne, attired in a violet tunic and red buskins with black bands.

A diadem of pearls is wreathed around his hair, which is arranged in symmetrical rolls. He has drooping eyelids, a straight nose, and a heavy and cunning expression of countenance. At the corners of the daïs, extended above his head, are placed four golden doves, and, at the foot of the throne, two enamelled lions are squatted. The doves begin to coo, the lions to roar. The Emperor rolls his eyes; Antony steps forward; and directly, without preamble, they proceed with a narrative of events.

"In the cities of Antioch, Ephesus, and Alexandria, the temples have been pillaged, and the statues of the gods converted into pots and porridge-pans."

The Emperor laughs heartily at this. Antony reproaches him for his tolerance towards the Novatians. But the Emperor flies into a passion. "Novatians, Arians, Meletians—he is sick of them all!" However, he admires the episcopacy, for the Christians create bishops, who depend on five or six personages, and it is his interest to gain over the latter in order to have the rest on his side. Moreover, he has not failed to furnish them with considerable sums. But he detests the fathers of the Council of Nicæa. "Come, let us have a look at them."

Antony follows him. And they are found on the same floor under a terrace which commands a view of a hippodrome full of people, and surmounted by porticoes wherein the rest of the crowd are walking to and fro. In the centre of the course there is a narrow platform on which stands a miniature temple of Mercury, a statue of Constantine, and three bronze serpents intertwined with each other; while at one end there are three huge wooden eggs, and at the other seven dolphins with their tails in the air.

Behind the Imperial pavilion, the prefects of the chambers, the lords of the household, and the Patri-

cians are placed at intervals as far as the first story of a church, all whose windows are lined with women. At the right is the gallery of the Blue faction, at the left that of the Green, while below there is a picket of soldiers, and, on a level with the arena, a row of Corinthian pillars, forming the entrance to the stalls.

The races are about to begin; the horses fall into line. Tall plumes fixed between their ears sway in the wind like trees; and in their leaps they shake the chariots in the form of shells, driven by coachmen wearing a kind of many-coloured cuirass with sleeves narrow at the wrists and wide in the arms, with legs uncovered, full beard, and hair shaven above the forehead after the fashion of the Huns.

Antony is deafened by the murmuring of voices. Above and below he perceives nothing but painted faces, motley garments, and plates of worked gold; and the sand of the arena, perfectly white, shines like a mirror.

The Emperor converses with him, confides to him some important secrets. informs him of the assassination of his own son Crispus, and goes so far as to consult Antony about his health.

Meanwhile, Antony perceives slaves at the end of the stalls. They are the fathers of the Council of Nicæa, in rags, abject. The martyr Paphnutius is brushing a horse's mane; Theophilus is scrubbing the legs of another; John is painting the hoofs of a third; while Alexander is picking up their droppings in a basket.

Antony passes among them. They salaam to him, beg of him to intercede for them, and kiss his hands. The entire crowd hoots at them; and he rejoices in their degradation immeasurably. And now he has become one of the great ones of the Court, the Emperor's confidant, first minister! Constantine places the diadem on his forehead, and Antony keeps it, as if this honour were quite natural to him.

And presently is disclosed, beneath the darkness, an immense hall, lighted up by candelabra of gold.

Columns, half lost in shadow so tall are they, run in a row behind the tables, which stretch to the horizon, where appear, in a luminous haze, staircases placed one above another, successions of archways, colossi, towers; and, in the background, an unoccupied wing of the palace, which cedars overtop, making blacker masses above the darkness.

The guests, crowned with violets, lean upon their elbows on low-lying couches. Beside each one are placed amphoræ, from which they pour out wine; and, at the very end, by himself, adorned with the tiara and covered with carbuncles, King Nebuchadnezzar is eating and drinking. To right and left of him, two theories of priests, with peaked caps, are swinging censers. Upon the ground are crawling captive kings, without feet or hands, to whom he flings bones to pick. Further down stand his brothers, with shades over their eyes, for they are perfectly blind.

A constant lamentation ascends from the depths of the ergastula. The soft and monotonous sounds of a hydraulic organ alternate with the chorus of voices; and one feels as if all around the hall there was an immense city, an ocean of humanity, whose waves were beating against the walls.

The slaves rush forward carrying plates. Women run about offering drink to the guests. The baskets groan under the load of bread, and a dromedary, laden with leathern bottles, passes to and fro, letting vervain trickle over the floor in order to cool it.

Belluarii lead forth lions; dancing-girls, with their hair in ringlets, turn somersaults, while squirting fire through their nostrils; negro-jugglers perform tricks; naked children fling snowballs, which, in falling, crash against the shining silver plate. The clamour is so dreadful that it might be described as a tempest, and the steam of the viands, as well as the respirations of the guests, spreads, as it were, a cloud over the feast. Now and then, flakes from the huge torches, snatched away by the wind, traverse the night like flying stars.

The King wipes off the perfumes from his visage with his hand. He eats from the sacred vessels, and then breaks them, and he enumerates, mentally, his fleets, his armies, his peoples. Presently, through a whim, he will burn his palace, along with his guests. He calculates on rebuilding the Tower of Babel, and dethroning God.

Antony reads, at a distance, on his forehead, all his thoughts. They take possession of himself—and he becomes Nebuchadnezzar.

Immediately, he is satiated with conquests and exterminations; and a longing seizes him to plunge into every kind of vileness. Moreover, the degradation wherewith men are terrified is an outrage done to their souls, a means still more of stupefying them; and, as nothing is lower than a brute beast, Antony falls upon four paws on the table, and bellows like a bull.

He feels a pain in his hand—a pebble, as it happened, has hurt him—and he again finds himself in his cell.

The rocky enclosure is empty. The stars are shining. All is silence.

"Once more I have been deceived. Why these things? They arise from the revolts of the flesh! Ah! miserable man that I am!"

He dashes into his cell, takes out of it a bundle of cords, with iron nails at the ends of them, strips himself to the waist, and raising his eyes towards Heaven:

"Accept my penance, O my God! Do not despise it on account of its insufficiency. Make it sharp, prolonged, excessive. It is time! To work!"

He proceeds to lash himself vigorously.

"Ah! no! no! No pity!"

He begins again.

"Oh! Oh! Oh! Each stroke tears my skin, cuts my limbs. This smarts horribly! Ah! it is not so terrible! One gets used to it. It seems to me even . . ."

Antony stops.

"Come on, then, coward! Come on, then! Good! good! On the arms, on the back, on the breast, against the belly, everywhere! Hiss, thongs! bite me! tear me! I would like the drops of my blood to gush forth to the stars, to break my back, to strip my nerves bare! Pincers! wooden horses! molten lead! The martyrs bore more than that! Is that not so, Ammonaria?"

The shadows of the Devil's horns reappear.

"I might have been fastened to the pillar next to yours, face to face with you, under your very eyes, responding to your shrieks with my sighs, and our griefs would blend into one, and our souls would commingle."

He flogs himself furiously.

"Hold! hold! for your sake! once more! . . . But this is a mere tickling that passes through my frame. What torture! What delight! Those are like kisses. My marrow is melting! I am dying!"

And in front of him he sees three cavaliers, mounted on wild asses, clad in green garments, holding lilies in their hands, and all resembling one another in figure.

Antony turns back, and sees three other cavaliers of the same kind, mounted on similar wild asses, in the same attitude.

He draws back. Then the wild asses, all at the same time, step forward a pace or two, and rub their snouts against him, trying to bite his garment. Voices exclaim, "This way! this way! Here is the place!" And banners appear between the clefts of the mountain, with camels' heads in halters of red silk, mules laden with baggage, and women covered with yellow veils, mounted astride on piebald horses.

The panting animals lie down; the slaves fling themselves on the bales of goods, roll out the variegated carpets, and strew the ground with glittering objects.

A white elephant, caparisoned with a fillet of gold, runs along, shaking the bouquet of ostrich feathers attached to his head-band.

On his back, lying on cushions of blue wool, cross-legged, with eyelids half-closed and well-poised head, is a woman so magnifiently attired that she emits rays around her. The attendants prostrate themselves, the elephant bends his knees, and the Queen of Sheba, gliding down by his shoulder, steps lightly on the carpet and advances towards Antony.

Her robe of gold brocade, regularly divided by furbelows of pearls, jet and sapphires, is drawn tightly round her waist by a close-fitting corsage, set off with a variety of colours representing the twelve signs of the Zodiac. She wears high-heeled pattens, one of which is black and strewn with silver stars and a crescent, whilst the other is white and is covered with drops of gold, with a sun in their midst.

Her loose sleeves, garnished with emeralds and birds' plumes, exposes to view her little, rounded arms, adorned at the wrists with bracelets of ebony; and her hands, covered with rings, are terminated by nails so pointed that the ends of her fingers are almost like needles.

A chain of plate gold, passing under her chin, runs along her cheeks till it twists itself in spiral fashion around her head, over which blue powder is scattered; then, descending, it slips over her shoulders and is fastened above her bosom by a diamond scorpion, which stretches out its tongue between her breasts. From her ears hang two great white pearls. The edges of her eyelids are painted black. On her left cheek-bone she has a natural brown spot, and when she opens her mouth she breathes with difficulty, as if her bodice distressed her.

As she comes forward, she swings a green parasol with an ivory handle surrounded by vermilion bells; and twelve curly negro boys carry the long train of her robe, the end of which is held by an ape, who raises it every now and then.

She says:

"Ah! handsome hermit! handsome hermit! My heart is faint! By dint of stamping with impatience my heels have grown hard, and I have split one of my toe-nails. I sent out shepherds, who posted themselves on the mountains, with their hands stretched over their eyes, and searchers, who cried out your name in the woods, and scouts, who ran along the different roads, saying to each passer-by: 'Have you seen him?'

"At night I shed tears with my face turned to the wall. My tears, in the long run, made two little holes in the mosaic-work—like pools of water in rocks—for I love you! Oh! yes; very much!"

She catches his beard.

"Smile on me, then, handsome hermit! Smile on me, then! You will find I am very gay! I play on the lyre, I dance like a bee, and I can tell many stories, each one more diverting than the last.

"You cannot imagine what a long journey we have made. Look at the wild asses of the green-clad couriers—dead through fatigue!"

The wild asses are stretched motionless on the ground.

"For three great moons they have journeyed at an even pace, with pebbles in their teeth to cut the wind, their tails always erect, their hams always bent, and always in full gallop. You will not find their equals. They came to me from my maternal grandfather, the Emperor Saharil, son of Jakhschab, son of Jaarab, son of Kastan. Ah! if they were still living, we would put them under a litter in order to get home quickly. But . . . how now? . . . What are you thinking of?"

She inspects him.

"Ah! when you are my husband, I will clothe you, I will fling perfumes over you, I will pick out your hairs."

Antony remains motionless, stiffer than a stake, pale as a corpse.

"You have a melancholy air: is it at quitting your cell? Why, I have given up everything for your sake—even King Solomon, who has, no doubt, much wisdom, twenty thousand war-chariots, and a lovely beard! I have brought you my wedding presents. Choose."

She walks up and down between the row of slaves and the merchandise.

"Here is balsam of Genesareth, incense from Cape Gardefan, ladanum, cinnamon and silphium, a good thing to put into sauces. There are within Assyrian embroideries, ivories from the Ganges, and the purple cloth of Elissa; and this case of snow contains a bottle of Chalybon, a wine reserved for the Kings of Assyria, which is drunk pure out of the horn of a unicorn. Here are collars, clasps, fillets, parasols, gold dust from Baasa, tin from Tartessus, blue wood from Pandion, white furs from Issidonia, carbuncles from the island of Palæsimundum, and tooth-picks made with the hair of the tachas—an extinct animal found under the earth. These cushions are from Emathia, and these mantle-fringes from Palmyra. Under this Babylonian carpet there are . . . but come, then! Come, then!"

She pulls Saint Antony along by the beard. He resists. She goes on:

"This light tissue, which crackles under the fingers with the noise of sparks, is the famous yellow linen brought by the merchants from Bactriana. They required no less than forty-three interpreters during their voyage. I will make garments of it for you, which you will put on at home.

"Press the fastenings of that sycamore box, and give me the ivory casket in my elephant's packing-case!"

They draw out of a box some round objects covered with a veil, and bring her a little case covered with carvings.

"Would you like the buckler of Dgian-ben-Dgian, the builder of the Pyramids? Here it is! It is composed of seven dragons' skins placed one above another, joined by diamond screws, and tanned in the bile of a parricide. It represents, on one side, all the wars which have taken place since the invention of arms, and, on the other, all the wars that will take place till the end of the world. Above, the thunderbolt rebounds like a ball of cork. I am going to put it on your arm, and you will carry it to the chase.

"But if you knew what I have in my little case! Try to open it! Nobody has succeeded in doing that. Embrace me, and I will tell you."

She takes Saint Antony by the two cheeks. He repels her with outstretched arms.

"It was one night when King Solomon had lost his head. At length, we had concluded a bargain. He arose, and, going out with the stride of a wolf . . ."

She dances a pirouette.

"Ah! ah! handsome hermit! you shall not know it! you shall not know it!"

She shakes her parasol, and all the little bells begin to ring.

"I have many other things besides — there, now! I have treasures shut up in galleries, where they are lost as in a wood. I have summer palaces of lattice-reeds, and winter palaces of black marble. In the midst of great lakes, like seas, I have islands round as pieces of silver all covered with mother-of-pearl, whose shores make music with the beating of the liquid waves that roll over the sand. The slaves of my kitchen catch birds in my aviaries, and angle for fish in my ponds. I have engravers continually sitting to stamp my likeness on hard stones, panting workers in bronze who cast my statues, and perfumers who mix the juice of plants with vinegar and beat up pastes. I have dressmakers who cut out stuffs for me, goldsmiths who make jewels for me, women whose duty it is to select head-dresses for me, and attentive house-painters pouring over my panellings boiling resin, which they cool with fans. I have attendants for my harem, eunuchs enough to make an army. And then I have armies, subjects! I have in my vestibule a guard of dwarfs, carrying on their backs ivory trumpets."

Antony sighs.

"I have teams of gazelles, quadrigæ of elephants, hundreds of camels, and mares with such long manes that their feet get entangled with them when they are galloping, and flocks with such huge horns that the woods are torn down in front of them when they are pasturing. I have giraffes who walk in my gardens, and who raise their heads over the edge of my roof when I am taking the air after dinner. Seated in a shell, and drawn by dolphins, I go up and down the grottoes, listening to the water flowing from the stalactites. I journey to the diamond country, where my friends the magicians allow me to choose the most beautiful; then I ascend to earth once more, and return home."

She gives a piercing whistle, and a large bird, descending from the sky, alights on the top of her head-dress, from which he scatters the blue powder. His plumage, of orange colour, seems composed of metallic scales. His dainty head, adorned with a silver tuft, exhibits a human visage. He has four wings, a vulture's claws, and an immense peacock's tail, which he displays in a ring behind him. He seizes in his beak the Queen's parasol, staggers a little before he finds his equilibrium, then erects all his feathers, and remains motionless.

"Thanks, fair Simorg-anka! You who have brought me to the place where the lover is concealed! Thanks! thanks! messenger of my heart! He flies like desire. He travels all over the world. In the evening he returns; he lies down at the foot of my couch; he tells me what he has seen, the seas he has flown over, with their fishes and their ships, the great empty deserts which he has looked down upon from his airy height in the skies, all the harvests bending in the fields, and the plants that shoot up on the walls of abandoned cities."

She twists her arms with a languishing air.

"Oh! if you were willing! if you were only willing! . . . I have a pavilion on a promontory, in the midst of an isthmus between two oceans. It is wainscotted with plates of glass, floored with tortoise-shells, and is open to the four winds of Heaven. From above, I watch the return of my fleets and the people who ascend the hill with loads on their shoulders. We should sleep on down softer than clouds; we should drink cool draughts out of the rinds of fruit, and we gaze at the sun through a canopy of emeralds. Come!"

Antony recoils.   She draws close to him, and, in a tone of irritation:

"How so? Rich, coquettish, and in love?—is not that enough for you, eh? But must she be lascivious, gross, with a hoarse voice, a head of hair like fire, and rebounding flesh? Do you prefer a body cold as a serpent's skin, or, perchance, great black eyes more sombre than mysterious caverns? Look at these eyes of mine, then!"

Antony gazes at them, in spite of himself.

"All the women you ever have met, from the daughter of the cross-roads singing beneath her lantern to the fair patrician scattering leaves from the top of her litter, all the forms you have caught a glimpse of, all the imaginings of your desire, ask for them! I am not a woman—I am a world. My garments have but to fall, and you shall discover upon my person a succession of mysteries."

Antony's teeth chattered.

"If you placed your finger on my shoulder, it would be like a stream of fire in your veins. The possession of the least part of my body will fill you with a joy more vehement than the conquest of an empire. Bring your lips near! My kisses have the taste of fruit which would melt in your heart. Ah! how you will lose yourself in my tresses, caress my breasts, marvel at my limbs, and be scorched by my eyes, between my arms, in a whirlwind——"

Antony makes the sign of the Cross.

"So, then, you disdain me! Farewell!"

She turns away weeping; then she returns.

"Are you quite sure? So lovely a woman?"

She laughs, and the ape who holds the end of her robe lifts it up.

"You will repent, my fine hermit! you will groan; you will be sick of life! but I will mock at you! la! la! la! oh! oh! oh!"

She goes off with her hands on her waist, skipping on one foot.

The slaves file off before Saint Antony's face, together with the horses, the dromedaries, the elephant, the attendants, the mules, once more covered with their loads, the negro boys, the ape, and the green-clad couriers holding their broken lilies in their hands —and the Queen of Sheba departs, with a spasmodic utterance which might be either a sob or a chuckle.

CHAPTER III.

The Disciple, Hilarion.

WHEN she has disappeared, Antony perceives a child on the threshold of his cell.

"It is one of the Queen's servants," he thinks.

This child is small, like a dwarf, and yet thickset, like one of the Cabiri, distorted, and with a miserable aspect. White hair covers his prodigiously large head, and he shivers under a sorry tunic, while he grasps in his hand a roll of papyrus. The light of the moon, across which a cloud is passing, falls upon him.

Antony observes him from a distance, and is afraid of him.

"Who are you?"

The child replies:

"Your former disciple, Hilarion."

Antony — "You lie! Hilarion has been living for many years in Palestine."

Hilarion — "I have returned from it! It is I, in good sooth!"

Antony, draws closer and inspects him — "Why, his figure was bright as the dawn, open, joyous. This one is quite sombre, and has an aged look."

(40)

Hilarion — "I am worn out with constant toiling."

Antony — "The voice, too, is different. It has a tone that chills you."

Hilarion — "That is because I nourish myself on bitter fare."

Antony — "And those white locks?"

Hilarion — "I have had so many griefs."

Antony, aside — "Can it be possible? . . ."

Hilarion — "I was not so far away as you imagined. The hermit, Paul, paid you a visit this year during the month of Schebar. It is just twenty days since the nomads brought you bread. You told a sailor the day before yesterday to send you three bodkins."

Antony — "He knows everything!"

Hilarion — "Learn, too, that I have never left you. But you spend long intervals without perceiving me."

Antony — "How is that? No doubt my head is troubled! To-night especially . . ."

Hilarion — "All the deadly sins have arrived. But their miserable snares are of no avail against a saint like you!"

Antony — "Oh! no! no! Every minute I give way! Would that I were one of those whose souls are always intrepid and their minds firm — like the great Athanasius, for example!"

Hilarion — "He was unlawfully ordained by seven bishops!"

Antony — "What does it matter? If his virtue . . ."

Hilarion — "Come, now! A haughty, cruel man, always mixed up in intrigues, and finally exiled for being a monopolist."

Antony — "Calumny!"

Hilarion — "You will not deny that he tried to corrupt Eustatius, the treasurer of the bounties?"

Antony — "So it is stated, and I admit it."

Hilarion — "He burned, for revenge, the house of Arsenius."

Antony — "Alas!"

Hilarion — "At the Council of Nicæa, he said, speaking of Jesus, 'The man of the Lord.'"

Antony — "Ah! that is a blasphemy!"

Hilarion — "So limited is he, too, that he acknowledges he knows nothing as to the nature of the Word."

Antony, smiling with pleasure — "In fact, he has not a very lofty intellect."

Hilarion — "If they had put you in his place, it would have been a great satisfaction for your brethren, as well as yourself. This life, apart from others, is a bad thing."

Antony — "On the contrary! Man, being a spirit, should withdraw himself from perishable things. All action degrades him. I would like not to cling to the earth—even with the soles of my feet."

Hilarion — "Hypocrite! who plunges himself into solitude to free himself the better from the outbreaks of his lusts! You deprive yourself of meat, of wine, of stoves, of slaves, and of honours; but how you let your imagination offer you banquets, perfumes, naked women, and applauding crowds! Your chastity is but a more subtle kind of corruption, and your contempt for the world is but the impotence of your hatred against it! This is the reason that persons like you are so lugubrious, or perhaps it is because they lack faith. The possession of the truth gives joy. Was Jesus sad? He used to go about surrounded by friends; He rested under the shade of the olive, entered the house of the publican, multiplied the cups, pardoned the fallen woman, healing all sorrows. As for you, you have no pity, save for your own wretchedness. You are so much swayed by a kind of remorse, and by a ferocious insanity, that you would repel the caress of a dog or the smile of a child."

Antony, bursts out sobbing—"Enough! Enough! You move my heart too much."

Hilarion—"Shake off the vermin from your rags! Get rid of your filth! Your God is not a Moloch who requires flesh as a sacrifice!"

Antony—"Still, suffering is blessed. The cherubim bend down to receive the blood of confessors."

Hilarion—"Then admire the Montanists! They surpass all the rest."

Antony—"But it is the truth of the doctrine that makes the martyr."

Hilarion—"How can he prove its excellence, seeing that he testifies equally on behalf of error?"

Antony—"Be silent, viper!"

Hilarion—"It is not perhaps so difficult. The exhortations of friends, the pleasure of outraging popular feeling, the oath they take, a certain giddy excitement—a thousand things, in fact, go to help them."

Antony draws away from Hilarion. Hilarion follows him—"Besides, this style of dying introduces great disorders. Dionysius, Cyprian, and Gregory avoided it. Peter of Alexandria has disapproved of it; and the Council of Elvira . . ."

Antony, stops his ears—"I will listen to no more!"

Hilarion, raising his voice—"Here you are again falling into your habitual sin—laziness. Ignorance is the froth of pride. You say, 'My conviction is formed; why discuss the matter?' and you despise the doctors, the philosophers, tradition, and even the text of the law, of which you know nothing. Do you think you hold wisdom in your hand?"

Antony—"I am always hearing him! His noisy words fill my head."

Hilarion—"The endeavours to comprehend God are better than your mortifications for the purpose of moving him. We have no merit save our thirst for truth. Religion alone does not explain everything; and the solution of the problems which you have ignored might render it more unassailable and more sublime. Therefore, it is essential for each man's salvation that he should hold intercourse with his brethren—otherwise the Church, the assembly of the faithful, would be only a word—and that he should listen to every argument, and not disdain anything, or anyone. Balaam the soothsayer, Æschylus the poet, and the sybil of Cumæ, announced the Saviour. Dionysius the Alexandrian received from Heaven a command to read every book. Saint Clement enjoins us to study Greek literature. Hermas was converted by the illusion of a woman that he loved!"

Antony—"What an air of authority! It appears to me that you are growing taller . . ."

In fact, Hilarion's height has progressively increased; and, in order not to see him, Antony closes his eyes.

Hilarion—"Make your mind easy, good hermit. Let us sit down here, on this big stone, as of yore, when, at the break of day, I used to salute you, addressing you as 'Bright morning star'; and you at once began to give me instruction. It is not finished yet. The moon affords us sufficient light. I am all attention."

He has drawn forth a calamus from his girdle, and, cross-legged on the ground, with his roll of papyrus in his hand, he raises his head towards Antony, who, seated beside him, keeps his forehead bent.

"Is not the word of God confirmed for us by the miracles? And yet the sorcerers of Pharaoh worked miracles. Other impostors could do the same; so here we may be deceived. What, then, is a miracle? An occurrence which seems to us outside the limits of Nature. But do we know all Nature's powers? And, from the mere fact that a thing ordinarily does not astonish us, does it follow that we comprehend it?"

Antony — "It matters little; we must believe in the Scripture."

Hilarion — "Saint Paul, Origen, and some others did not interpret it literally; but, if we explain it allegorically, it becomes the heritage of a limited number of people, and the evidence of its truth vanishes. What are we to do, then?"

Antony — "Leave it to the Church."

Hilarion — "Then the Scripture is useless?"

Antony — "Not at all. Although the Old Testament, I admit, has — well, obscurities . . . But the New shines forth with a pure light."

Hilarion — "And yet the Angel of the Annunciation, in Matthew, appears to Joseph, whilst in Luke it is to Mary. The anointing of Jesus by a woman comes to pass, according to the First Gospel, at the beginning of his public life, but according to the three others, a few days before his death. The drink which they offer him on the Cross is, in Matthew, vinegar and gall, in Mark, wine and myrrh. If we follow Luke and Matthew, the Apostles ought to take neither money nor bag — in fact, not even sandals or a staff; while in Mark, on the contrary, Jesus forbids them to carry with them anything except sandals and a staff. Here is where I get lost. . . ."

Antony, in amazement — "In fact . . . in fact . . ."

Hilarion — "At the contact of the woman with the issue of blood, Jesus turned round, and said, 'Who has touched me?' So, then, He did not know who touched Him? That is opposed to the omniscience of Jesus. If the tomb was watched by guards, the women had not to worry themselves about an assistant to lift up the stone from the tomb. Therefore, there were no guards there — or rather, the holy women were not there at all. At Emmaüs, He eats with His disciples, and makes them feel His wounds. It is a human body, a material object, which can be weighed, and which, nevertheless, passes through stone walls. Is this possible?"

Antony — "It would take a good deal of time to answer you."

Hilarion — "Why did He receive the Holy Ghost, although He was the Son? What need had He of baptism, if He were the Word? How could the Devil tempt Him — God?

"Have these thoughts never occurred to you?"

Antony — "Yes! often! Torpid or frantic, they dwell in my conscience. I crush them out; they spring up again, they stifle me; and sometimes I believe that I am accursed."

Hilarion — "Then you have nothing to do but to serve God?"

Antony—"I have always need to adore Him."

After a prolonged silence, Hilarion resumes:

"But apart from dogma, entire liberty of research is permitted us. Do you wish to become acquainted with the hierarchy of Angels, the virtue of Numbers, the explanation of germs and metamorphoses?"

Antony—"Yes! yes! My mind is struggling to escape from its prison. It seems to me that, by gathering my forces, I shall be able to effect this. Sometimes—even for an interval brief as a lightning-flash—I feel myself, as it were, suspended in midair; then I fall back again!"

Hilarion—"The secret which you are anxious to possess is guarded by sages. They live in a distant country, sitting under gigantic trees, robed in white, and calm as gods. A warm atmosphere nourishes them. All around leopards stride through the plains. The murmuring of fountains mingles with the neighing of unicorns. You shall hear them; and the face of the Unknown shall be unveiled!"

Antony, sighing—"The road is long and I am old!"

Hilarion—"Oh! oh! men of learning are not rare! There are some of them even very close to you here! Let us enter!"

CHAPTER IV.

The Fiery Trial.

AND Antony sees in front of him an immense basilica. The light projects itself from the lower end with the magical effect of a many-coloured sun. It lights up the innumerable heads of the multitude which fills the nave and surges between the columns towards the side-aisles, where one can distinguish in the wooden compartments altars, beds, chainlets of little blue stones, and constellations painted on the walls.

In the midst of the crowd groups are stationed here and there; men standing on stools are discoursing with lifted fingers; others are praying with arms crossed, or lying down on the ground, or singing hymns, or drinking wine. Around a table the faithful are carrying on the love-feasts; martyrs are unswathing their limbs to show their wounds; old men, leaning on their staffs, are relating their travels.

Amongst them are people from the country of the Germans, from Thrace, Gaul, Scythia and the Indies —with snow on their beards, feathers in their hair, thorns in the fringes of their garments, sandals covered with dust, and skins burnt by the sun. All costumes are mingled — mantles of purple and robes of linen, embroidered dalmatics, woollen jackets, sailors' caps and bishops' mitres. Their eyes gleam strangely. They have the appearance of executioners or of eunuchs.

Hilarion advances among them. Antony, pressing against his shoulder, observes them. He notices a great many women. Several of them are dressed like men, with their hair cut short. He is afraid of them.

Hilarion — "These are the Christian women who have converted their husbands. Besides, the women are always for Jesus — even the idolaters — as witness Procula, the wife of Pilate, and Poppæa, the concubine of Nero. Don't tremble any more! Come on!"

There are fresh arrivals every moment.

They multiply; they separate, swift as shadows, all the time making a great uproar, or intermingling yells of rage, exclamations of love, canticles, and upbraidings.

Antony, in a low tone — "What do they want?"

Hilarion — "The Lord said, 'I may still have to speak to you about many things.' They possess those things."

And he pushes him towards a throne of gold, five paces off, where, surrounded by ninety-five disciples, all anointed with oil, pale and emaciated, sits the prophet Manes — beautiful as an archangel, motionless as a statue — wearing an Indian robe, with carbuncles in his plaited hair, a book of coloured pictures in his left hand, and a globe under his right. The pictures represent the creatures who are slumbering in chaos. Antony bends forward to see him. Then

Manes makes his globe revolve, and, attuning his words to the music of a lyre, from which bursts forth crystalline sounds, he says:

·"The celestial earth is at the upper extremity, the mortal earth at the lower. It is supported by two angels, the Splenditenens and the Omophorus, with six faces.

"At the summit of Heaven, the Impassible Divinity occupies the highest seat; underneath, face to face, are the Son of God and the Prince of Darkness.

"The darkness having made its way into His kingdom, God extracted from His essence a virtue which produced the first man; and He surrounded him with five elements. But the demons of darkness deprived him of one part, and that part is the soul.

"There is but one soul, spread through the universe, like the water of a stream divided into many channels. This it is that sighs in the wind, grinds in the marble which is sawn, howls in the voice of the sea; and it sheds milky tears when the leaves are torn off the fig-tree.

"The souls that leave this world emigrate towards the stars, which are animated beings."

Antony begins to laugh:

"Ah! ah! what an absurd hallucination!"

A man, beardless, and of austere aspect—"Why?"

Antony is about to reply. But Hilarion tells him in an undertone, that this man is the mighty Origen; and Manes resumes:

"At first, they stay in the moon, where they are purified. After that, they ascend to the sun."

Antony, slowly—"I know nothing to prevent us from believing it."

Manes — "The end of every creature is the liberation of the celestial ray shut up in matter. It makes its escape more easily through perfumes, spices, the aroma of old wine, the light substances that resemble thought. But the actions of daily life withhold it. The murderer will be born again in the body of a eunuch; he who slays an animal will become that animal. If you plant a vine-tree, you will be fastened in its branches. Food absorbs those who use it. Therefore, mortify yourselves! fast!"

Hilarion — "They are temperate, as you see!"

Manes — "There is a great deal of it in flesh-meats, less in herbs. Besides, the Pure, by the force of their merits, despoil vegetables of that luminous spark, and it flies towards its source. The animals, by generation, imprison it in the flesh. Therefore, avoid women!"

Hilarion — "Admire their countenance!"

Manes — "Or, rather, act so well that they may not be prolific. It is better for the soul to sink on the earth than to languish in carnal fetters."

Antony — "Ah! abomination!"

Hilarion — "What matters the hierarchy of iniquities? The Church has done well to make marriage a sacrament!"

Saturninus, in Syrian costume — "He propagates a dismal order of things! The Father, in order to punish the rebel angels, commanded them to create the world. Christ came in order that the God of the Jews, who was one of those angels——"

Antony — "An angel? He! the Creator?"

Gerdon — "Did He not desire to kill Moses and deceive the prophets? and did He not lead the people astray, spreading lying and idolatry?"

Marcion—"Certainly, the Creator is not the true God!"

Saint Clement of Alexandria—"Matter is eternal!"

Bardesanes, as one of the Babylonian Magi—"It was formed by the seven planetary spirits."

The Hernians—"The angels have made the souls!"

The Priscillianists—"The world was made by the Devil."

Antony, falls backward—"Horror!"

Hilarion, holding him up—"You drive yourself to despair too quickly! You don't rightly comprehend their doctrine. Here is one who has received his from Theodas, the friend of Saint Paul. Hearken to him!"

And, at a signal from Hilarion, Valentinus, in a tunic of silver cloth, with a hissing voice and a pointed skull, cries:

"The world is the work of a delirious God!"

Antony, hangs down his head—"The work of a delirious God!"

After a long silence:

"How is that?"

Valentinus—"The most perfect of the Æons, the Abysm, reposed on the bosom of Profundity together with Thought. From their union sprang Intelligence, who had for his consort Truth.

"Intelligence and Truth engendered the Word and Life, which in their turn engendered Man and the Church; and this makes eight Æons."

He reckons on his fingers:

"The Word and Truth produced ten other Æons, that is to say, five couples. Man and the Church produced twelve others, amongst whom were the Paraclete and Faith, Hope and Charity, Perfection and Wisdom, Sophia.

"The entire of those thirty Æons constitutes the Pleroma, or Universality of God. Thus, like the echoes of a voice that is dying away, like the exhalations of a perfume that is evaporating, like the fires of a sun that is setting, the Powers that have emanated from the Highest Powers are always growing feeble.

"But Sophia, desirous of knowing the Father, rushed out of the Pleroma; and the Word then made another pair, Christ and the Holy Ghost, who bound together all the Æons, and all together they formed Jesus, the flower of the Pleroma. Meanwhile, the effort of Sophia to escape had left in the void an image of her, an evil substance, Acharamoth. The Saviour took pity on her, and delivered her from her passions; and from the smile of Acharamoth on being set free Light was born; her tears made the waters, and her sadness engendered gloomy Matter. From Acharamoth sprang the Demiurge, the fabricator of the worlds, the heavens, and the Devil. He dwells much lower down than the Pleroma, without even beholding it, so that he imagines he is the true God, and repeats through the mouths of his prophets: 'Besides me there is no God.' Then he made man, and cast into his soul the immaterial seed, which was the Church, the reflection of the other Church placed in the Pleroma.

"Acharamoth, one day, having reached the highest region, shall unite with the Saviour; the fire hidden in the world shall annihilate all matter, shall then consume itself, and men, having become pure spirits, shall espouse the angels!"

Origen — "Then the Demon shall be conquered, and the reign of God shall begin!"

Antony represses an exclamation, and immediately Basilides, catching him by the elbow:

"The Supreme Being, with his infinite emanations, is called Abraxas, and the Saviour with all his virtues, Kaulakau, otherwise rank-upon-rank, rectitude-upon-rectitude. The power of Kaulakau is obtained by the aid of certain words inscribed on this calcedony to facilitate memory."

And he shows on his neck a little stone on which fantastic lines are engraved.

"Then you shall be transported into the invisible; and, unfettered by law, you shall despise everything, including virtue itself. As for us, the Pure, we must avoid sorrow, after the example of Kaulakau."

Antony—"What! and the Cross?"

The Elkhesaites, in hyacinthine robes, reply to him:

"The sadness, the vileness, the condemnation, and the oppression of my fathers are effaced, thanks to the new Gospel. We may deny the inferior Christ, the man-Jesus; but we must adore the other Christ generated in his person under the wing of the Dove. Honour marriage! The Holy Spirit is feminine!"

Hilarion has disappeared; and Antony, pressed forward by the crowd, finds himself facing the Carpocratians, stretched with women upon scarlet cushions:

"Before re-entering the centre of unity, you will have to pass through a series of conditions and actions. In order to free yourself from the Powers of Darkness, do their works for the present! The husband goes to his wife and says, 'Act with charity towards your brother,' and she will kiss you."

The Nicolaites, assembled around a smoking dish:

"This is meat offered to idols; let us take it! Apostacy is permitted when the heart is pure. Glut your flesh with what it asks for. Try to destroy it by means of debaucheries. Prounikos, the mother of Heaven, wallows in iniquity."

The Marcosians, with rings of gold and dripping with balsam:

"Come to us, in order to be united with the Spirit! Come to us, in order to drink immortality!"

And one of them points out to him, behind some tapestry, the body of a man with an ass's head. This represents Sabaoth, the father of the Devil. As a mark of hatred he spits upon it.

Another discloses a very low bed strewn with flowers, saying as he does so:

"The spiritual nuptials are about to be consummated."

A third holds forth a goblet of glass while he utters an invocation. Blood appears in it:

"Ah! there it is! there it is! the blood of Christ!"

Antony turns aside; but he is splashed by the water, which leaps out of a tub.

The Helvidians cast themselves into it head foremost, muttering:

"Man regenerated by baptism is incapable of sin!"

Then he passes close to a great fire, where the Adamites are warming themselves completely naked to imitate the purity of Paradise; and he jostles up against the Messalians wallowing on the stone floor half-asleep, stupid:

"Oh! run over us, if you like; we shall not budge! Work is a sin; all occupation is evil!"

Behind those, the abject Paternians, men, women, and children, pell-mell, on a heap of filth, lift up their hideous faces, besmeared with wine:

"The inferior parts of the body, having been made by the Devil, belong to him. Let us eat, drink, and enjoy!"

Ætius—"Crimes come from the need here below of the love of God!"

But all at once a man, clad in a Carthaginian mantle, jumps among them, with a bundle of thongs in his hand; and striking at random to right and left of him violently:

"Ah! imposters, brigands, simoniacs, heretics, and demons! the vermin of the schools! the dregs of Hell! This fellow here, Marcion, is a sailor from Sinope excommunicated for incest. Carpocras has been banished as a magician; Ætius has stolen his concubine; Nicolas prostituted his own wife; and Manes, who describes himself as the Buddha, and whose name is Cubricus, was flayed with the sharp end of a cane, so that his tanned skin swings at the gates of Ctesiphon."

Antony has recognised Tertullian, and rushes forward to meet him.

"Help, master! help!"

Tertullian, continuing—"Break the images! Veil the virgins! Pray, fast, weep, mortify yourselves! No philosophy! no books! After Jesus, science is useless!"

All have fled; and Antony sees, instead of Tertullian, a woman seated on a stone bench. She sobs, her head resting against a pillar, her hair hanging down, and her body wrapped in a long brown simar.

Then they find themselves close to each other far from the crowd; and a silence, an extraordinary peacefulness, ensues, such as one feels in a wood when the wind ceases and the leaves flutter no longer.

This woman is very beautiful, though faded and pale as death. They stare at each other, and their eyes mutually exchange a flood of thoughts, as it were, a thousand memories of the past, bewildering and profound. At last Priscilla begins to speak:

"I was in the lowest chamber of the baths, and I was lulled to sleep by the confused murmurs that reached me from the streets. All at once I heard loud exclamations. The people cried, 'It is a magician! it is the Devil!' And the crowd stopped in front of our house opposite to the Temple of Æsculapius. I raised myself with my wrists to the height of the air-hole. On the peristyle of the temple was a man with an iron collar around his neck. He placed lighted coals on a chafing-dish, and with them made large furrows on his breast, calling out, 'Jesus! Jesus!' The people said, 'That is not lawful! let us stone him!' But he did not desist. The things that were occurring were unheard of, astounding. Flowers, large as the sun, turned around before my eyes, and I heard a harp of gold vibrating in mid-air. The day sank to its close. My arms let go the iron bars; my strength was exhausted; and when he bore me away to his house——"

Antony—"Whom are you talking about?"

Priscilla—"Why, of Montanus!"

Antony—"But Montanus is dead."

Priscilla—"That is not true."

A voice—"No, Montanus is not dead!"

Antony comes back; and near him, on the other side upon a bench, a second woman is seated—this one being fair, and paler still, with swellings under her eyelids, as if she had been a long time weeping. Without waiting for him to question her, she says:

Maximilla—"We were returning from Tarsus by the mountains, when, at a turn of the road, we saw a man under a fig-tree. He cried from a distance, 'Stop!' and he sprang forward, pouring out abuse on us. The slaves rushed up to protect us. He burst out laughing. The horses pranced. The mastiffs all began to howl. He was standing up. The perspiration fell down his face. The wind made his cloak flap.

"While addressing us by name, he reproached us for the vanity of our actions, the impurity of our bodies; and he raised his fist towards the dromedaries on account of the silver bells which they wore under their jaws. His fury filled my very entrails with terror; nevertheless, it was a voluptuous sensation, which soothed, intoxicated me. At first, the slaves drew near. 'Master,' said they, 'our beasts are fatigued'; then there were the women: 'We are frightened'; and the slaves ran away. After that, the children began to cry, 'We are hungry.' And, as no answer was given to the women, they disappeared. And now he began to speak. I perceived that there was some one close beside me. It was my husband: I listened to the other. The first crawled between the stones, exclaiming, 'Do you abandon me?' and I replied, 'Yes! begone!' in order to accompany Montanus."

Antony—"A eunuch!"

Priscilla—"Ah! coarse heart, you are astonished at this! Yet Magdalen, Jane, Martha and Susanna did not enter the couch of the Saviour. Souls can be madly embraced more easily than bodies. In order to retain Eustolia with impunity, the Bishop Leontius mutilated himself—cherishing his love more than his virility. And, then, it is not my own fault. A spirit compels me to do it; Eotas cannot cure me. Nevertheless, he is cruel. What does it matter? I am the last of the prophetesses; and, after me, the end of the world will come."

Maximilla—"He has loaded me with his gifts. None of the others loved me so much, nor is any of them better loved."

Priscilla—"You lie! I am the person he loves!"

Maximilla—"No: it is I!"

They fight.

Between their shoulders appears a negro's head.

Montanus, covered with a black cloak, fastened by two dead men's bones:

"Be quiet, my doves! Incapable of terrestrial happiness, we by this union attain to spiritual plenitude. After the age of the Father, the age of the Son; and I inaugurate the third, that of the Paraclete. His light came to me during the forty nights when the heavenly Jerusalem shone in the firmament above my house at Pepuza.

"Ah! how you cry out with anguish when the thongs flagellate you! How your aching limbs offer themselves to my burning caresses! How you languish upon my breast with an inconceivable love! It is so strong that it has revealed new worlds to you, and you can now behold spirits with your mortal eyes."

Antony makes a gesture of astonishment.

Tertullian, coming up close to Montanus—"No doubt, since the soul has a body, that which has no body exists not."

Montanus—"In order to render it less material I have introduced numerous mortifications·—three Lents

7—5

every year, and, for each night, prayers, in saying
which the mouth is kept closed, for fear the breath,
in escaping, should sully the mental act. It is necessary to abstain from second marriages — or, rather,
from marriage altogether! The angels sinned with
women."

The Archontics, in hair-shirts:

"The Saviour said, 'I came to destroy the work
of the woman.'"

The Tatianists, in hair-cloths of rushes:

"She is the tree of evil! Our bodies are the garments of skin."

And, ever advancing on the same side, Antony en-
counters the Valesians, stretched on the ground, with
red plates below their stomachs, beneath their tunics.

They present to him a knife.

"Do like Origen and like us! Is it the pain you
fear, coward? Is it the love of your flesh that restrains you, hypocrite?"

And while he watches them struggling, extended
on their backs swimming in their own blood, the
Cainites, with their hair fastened by vipers, pass close
to him, shouting in his ears:

"Glory to Cain! Glory to Sodom! Glory to
Judas!

"Cain begot the race of the strong; Sodom terrified the earth with its chastisement, and it is through
Judas that God saved the world! Yes, Judas! without him no death and no Redemption!"

They pass out through the band of Circoncellions,
clad in wolf-skin, crowned with thorns, and carrying
iron clubs.

"Crush the fruit! Attack the fountain-head!
Drown the child! Plunder the rich man who is

happy, and who eats overmuch! Strike down the poor man who casts an envious glance at the ass's saddle-cloth, the dog's meal, the bird's nest, and who is grieved at not seeing others as miserable as himself.

"As for us—the Saints—in order to hasten the end of the world, we poison, burn, massacre. The only salvation is in martyrdom. We give ourselves up to martyrdom. We take off with pincers the skin of our heads; we spread our limbs under the ploughs; we cast ourselves into the mouths of furnaces. Shame on baptism! Shame on the Eucharist! Shame on marriage! Universal damnation!"

Then, throughout the basilica, there is a fresh accession of frenzy. The Audians draw arrows against the Devil; the Collyridians fling blue veils to the ceiling; the Ascitians prostrate themselves before a wineskin; the Marcionites baptise a corpse with oil. Close beside Appelles, a woman, the better to explain her idea, shows a round loaf of bread in a bottle; another, surrounded by the Sampsians, distributes like a host the dust of her sandals. On the bed of the Marcosians, strewn with roses, two lovers embrace each other. The Circoncellions cut one another's throats; the Velesians make a rattling sound; Bardesanes sings; Carpocras dances; Maximilla and Priscilla utter loud groans; and the false prophetess of Cappadocia, quite naked, resting on a lion and brandishing three torches, yells forth the Terrible Invocation.

The pillars are poised like trunks of trees; the amulets round the necks of the Heresiarchs have lines of flame crossing each other; the constellations in the chapels move to and fro, and the walls recede under the alternate motion of the crowd, in which every head is a wave which leaps and roars.

Meanwhile, from the very depths of the uproar rises a song with bursts of laughter, in which the name of Jesus recurs. These outbursts come from the common people, who all clap their hands in order to keep time with the music. In the midst of them is Arius, in the dress of a deacon:

"The fools who declaim against me pretend to explain the absurd; and, in order to destroy them entirely, I have composed little poems so comical that they are known by heart in the mills, the taverns, and the ports.

"A thousand times no! the Son is not co-eternal with the Father, nor of the same substance. Otherwise He would not have said, 'Father, remove from Me this chalice! Why do ye call Me good? God alone is good! I go to my God, to your God!' and other expressions, proving that He was a created being. It is demonstrated to us besides by all His names: lamb, shepherd, fountain, wisdom, Son of Man, prophet, good way, corner-stone."

Sabellius — "As for me, I maintain that both are identical."

Arius — "The Council of Antioch has decided the other way."

Antony — "Who, then, is the Word? Who was Jesus?"

The Valentinians — "He was the husband of Acharamoth when she had repented!"

The Sethianians — "He was Sem, son of Noah!"

The Theodotians — "He was Melchisidech!"

The Merinthians — "He was nothing but a man!"

The Apollonarists — "He assumed the appearance of one! He simulated the Passion!"

Marcellus of Ancyra — "He is a development of the Father!"

Pope Calixtus—"Father and Son are the two forms of a single God!"

Methadius—"He was first in Adam, and then in man!"

Cerinthus—"And He will come back to life again!"

Valentinus—"Impossible—His body is celestial."

Paul of Samosta—"He is God only since His baptism."

Hermogenes—"He dwells in the sun."

And all the heresiarchs form a circle around Antony, who weeps, with his head in his hands.

A Jew, with red beard, and his skin spotted with leprosy, advances close to him, and chuckling horribly:

"His soul was the soul of Esau. He suffered from the disease of Bellerophon; and his mother, the woman who sold perfumes, surrendered herself to Pantherus, a Roman soldier, under the corn-sheaves, one harvest evening."

Antony eagerly lifts up his head, and gazes at them without uttering a word; then, treading right over them:

"Doctors, magicians, bishops and deacons, men and phantoms, back! back! Ye are all lies!"

The Heresiarchs—"We have martyrs, more martyrs than yours, prayers more difficult, higher outbursts of love, and ecstasies quite as protracted."

Antony—"But no revelation. No proofs."

Then all brandish in the air rolls of papyrus, tablets of wood, pieces of leather, and strips of cloth; and pushing them one before the other:

The Corinthians—"Here is the Gospel of the Hebrews!"

The Marcionites—"The Gospel of the Lord! The Gospel of Eve!"

The Encratites—"The Gospel of Thomas!"

The Cainites—"The Gospel of Judas!"

Basilides—"The treatise of the spirit that has come!"

Manes—"The prophecy of Barcouf!"

Antony makes a struggle and escapes them, and he perceives, in a corner filled with shadows, the old Ebionites, dried up like mummies, their glances dull, their eyebrows white.

They speak in a quavering tone:

"We have known, we ourselves have known, the carpenter's son. We were of his own age; we lived in his street. He used to amuse himself by modelling little birds with mud; without being afraid of cutting the benches, he assisted his father in his work, or rolled up, for his mother, balls of dyed wool. Then he made a journey into Egypt, whence he brought back wonderful secrets. We were in Jericho when he discovered the eater of grasshoppers. They talked together in a low tone, without anyone being able to hear them. But it was since that occurrence that he made a noise in Galilee and that many stories have been circulated concerning him."

They repeat, tremulously:

"We have known, we ourselves; we have known him."

Antony—"One moment! Tell me! pray tell me, what was his face like?"

Tertullian—"Fierce and repulsive in its aspect; for he was laden with all the crimes, all the sorrows, and all the deformities of the world."

Antony—"Oh! no! no! I imagine, on the contrary, that there was about his entire person a super-human beauty."

Eusebius of Cæsarea — "There is at Paneadæ, close to an old ruin, in the midst of a rank growth of weeds, a statue of stone, raised, as it is pretended, by the woman with the issue of blood. But time has gnawed away the face, and the rain has obliterated the inscription."

A woman comes forth from the group of Carpocratians.

Marcellina — "I was formerly a deaconess in a little church at Rome, where I used to show the faithful images, in silver, of St. Paul, Homer, Pythagoras and Jesus Christ.

"I have kept only his."

She draws aside the folds of her cloak.

"Do you wish it?"

A voice — "He reappears himself when we invoke him. It is the hour. Come!"

And Antony feels a brutal hand laid on him, which drags him along.

He ascends a staircase in complete darkness, and, after proceeding for some time, arrives in front of a door. Then his guide (is it Hilarion? he cannot tell) says in the ear of a third person, "The Lord is about to come," — and they are introduced into an apartment with a low ceiling and no furniture. What strikes him at first is, opposite him, a long chrysalis of the colour of blood, with a man's head, from which rays escape, and the word *Knouphis* written in Greek all around. It rises above a shaft of a column placed in the midst of a pedestal. On the other walls of the apartment, medallions of polished brass represent heads of animals — that of an ox, of a lion, of an eagle, of a dog, and again, an ass's head! The argil lamps, suspended below these images, shed a flickering light. Antony, through a hole in the wall, perceives the moon, which shines far away on the waves, and he can even distinguish their monotonous ripple, with the dull sound of a ship's keel striking against the stones of a pier.

Men, squatting on the ground, their faces hidden beneath their cloaks, give vent at intervals to a kind of stifled barking. Women are sleeping, with their foreheads clasped by both arms, which are supported by their knees, so completely shrouded by their veils that one would say they were heaps of clothes arranged along the wall. Beside them, children, half-naked, and half devoured with vermin, watch the lamps burning, with an idiotic air; — and they are doing nothing; they are awaiting something.

They speak in low voices about their families, or communicate to one another remedies for their diseases. Many of them are going to embark at the end of the day, the persecution having become too severe. The Pagans, however, are not hard to deceive. "They believe, the fools, that we adore Knouphis!"

But one of the brethren, suddenly inspired, places himself in front of the column, where they have laid a loaf of bread, which is on the top of a basket full of fennel and hartwort.

The others have taken their places, forming, as they stand, three parallel lines.

The inspired one unrolls a paper covered with cylinders joined together, and then begins:

"Upon the darkness the ray of the Word descended, and a violent cry burst forth, which seemed like the voice of light."

All responding, while they sway their bodies to and fro:

"Kyrie eleison!"

The inspired one—"Man, then, was created by the infamous God of Israel, with the assistance of those here,"—pointing towards the medallions—"Aristophaios, Oraios, Sabaoth, Adonai, Eloi and Iaô!

"And he lay on the mud, hideous, feeble, shapeless, without the power of thought."

All, in a plaintive tone:

"Kyrie eleison!"

The inspired one—"But Sophia, taking pity on him, quickened him with a portion of her spirit. Then, seeing man so beautiful, God was seized with anger, and imprisoned him in His kingdom, interdicting him from the tree of knowledge. Still, once more, the other one came to his aid. She sent the serpent, who, with its sinuous advances, prevailed on him to disobey this law of hate. And man, when he had tasted knowledge, understood heavenly matters."

All, with energy:

"Kyrie eleison!"

The inspired one—"But Jaldalaoth, in order to be revenged, plunged man into matter, and the serpent along with him!"

All, in very low tones:

"Kyrie eleison!"

They close their mouths and then become silent.

The odours of the harbour mingle in the warm air with the smoke of the lamps. Their wicks, spluttering, are on the point of being extinguished, and long mosquitoes flutter around them. Antony gasps with anguish. He has the feeling that some monstrosity is floating around him—the horror of a crime about to be perpetrated.

But the inspired one, stamping with his feet, snapping his fingers, tossing his head, sings a psalm, with a wild refrain, to the sound of cymbals and of a shrill flute:

"Come! come! come! come forth from thy cavern!

"Swift One, that runs without feet, captor that takes without hands! Sinuous as the waves, round as the sun, darkened with spots of gold; like the firmament, strewn with stars! like the twistings of the vine-tree and the windings of entrails!

"Unbegotten! earth-devourer! ever young! perspicacious! honoured at Epidaurus! good for men! who cured King Ptolemy, the soldiers of Moses, and Glaucus, son of Minos!

"Come! come! come! come forth from thy cavern!"
All repeat:

"Come! come! come! come forth from thy cavern!"
However, there is no manifestation.

"Why, what is the matter with him?"

They proceed to deliberate, and to make suggestions. One old man offers a clump of grass. Then there is a rising in the basket. The green herbs are agitated; the flowers fall, and the head of a python appears.

He passes slowly over the edge of the loaf, like a circle turning round a motionless disc; then he develops, lengthens; he becomes of enormous weight. To prevent him from grazing the ground, the men support him with their breasts, the women with their heads, and the children with the tips of their fingers; and his tail, emerging through the hole in the wall, stretches out indefinitely, even to the depths of the sea. His rings unfold themselves, and fill the apartment. They wind themselves round Antony.

The Faithful, pressing their mouths against his skin, snatch the bread which he has nibbled.

"It is thou! it is thou!

"Raised at first by Moses, crushed by Ezechias, re-established by the Messiah. He drank thee in the waters of baptism; but thou didst quit him in the Garden of Olives, and then he felt all his weakness.

"Writhing on the bar of the Cross, and higher than his head, slavering above the crown of thorns, thou didst behold him dying; for thou art Jesus! yes, thou art the Word! thou art the Christ!"

Antony swoons in horror, and falls in his cell, upon the splinters of wood, where the torch, which had slipped from his hand, is burning mildly. This commotion causes him to half-open his eyes; and he perceives the Nile, undulating and clear, under the light of the moon, like a great serpent in the midst of the sands—so much so that the hallucination again takes possession of him. He has not quitted the Ophites; they surround him, address him by name, carry off baggages, and descend towards the port. He embarks along with them.

A brief period of time flows by. Then the vault of a prison encircles him. In front of him, iron bars make black lines upon a background of blue; and at its sides, in the shade, are people weeping and praying, surrounded by others who are exhorting and consoling them.

Without, one is attracted by the murmuring of a crowd, as well as by the splendour of a summer's day. Shrill voices are crying out watermelons, water, iced drinks, and cushions of grass to sit down on. From time to time, shouts of applause burst forth. He observes people walking on their heads.

Suddenly, comes a continuous roaring, strong and cavernous, like the noise of water in an aqueduct;

and, opposite him, he perceives, behind the bars of another cage, a lion, who is walking up and down; then a row of sandals, of naked legs, and of purple fringes.

Overhead, groups of people, ranged symmetrically, widen out from the lowest circle, which encloses the arena, to the highest, where masts have been raised to support a veil of hyacinth hung in the air on ropes. Staircases, which radiate towards the centre, intersect, at equal distances, those great circles of stone. Their steps disappear from view, owing to the vast audience seated there — knights, senators, soldiers, common people, vestals and courtesans, in woollen hoods, in silk maniples, in tawny tunics with aigrettes of precious stones, tufts of feathers and lictors' rods; and all this assemblage, muttering, exclaiming, tumultuous and frantic, stuns him like an immense tub boiling over. In the midst of the arena, upon an altar, smokes a vessel of incense.

The people who surround him are Christians, delivered up to the wild beasts. The men wear the red cloak of the high-priests of Saturn, the women the fillets of Ceres. Their friends distribute fragments of their garments and rings. In order to gain admittance into the prison, they require, they say, a great deal of money; but what does it matter? They will remain till the end.

Amongst these consolers Antony observes a bald man in a black tunic, a portion of whose face is plainly visible. He discourses with them on the nothingness of the world, and the happiness of the Elect. Antony is filled with transports of Divine love. He longs for the opportunity of sacrificing his life for the Saviour, not knowing whether he is himself one of these martyrs. But, save a Phrygian, with long hair, who keeps his arms raised, they all have a melancholy aspect. An old man is sobbing on a bench, and a young man, who is standing, is musing with downcast eyes.

The old man has refused to pay tribute at the angle of a cross-road, before a statue of Minerva; and he regards his companions with a look which signifies:

"You ought to succour me! Communities sometimes make arrangements by which they might be left in peace. Many amongst you have even obtained letters falsely declaring that you have offered sacrifice to idols."

He asks:

"Is it not Peter of Alexandria who has regulated what one ought to do when one is overcome by tortures?"

Then, to himself:

"Ah! this is very hard at my age! my infirmities render me so feeble! Perchance, I might have lived to another winter!"

The recollection of his little garden moves him to tears; and he contemplates the side of the altar.

The young man, who had disturbed by violence a feast of Apollo, murmurs:

"My only chance was to fly to the mountains!"

"The soldiers would have caught you," says one of the brethren.

"Oh! I could have done like Cyprian; I should have come back; and the second time I should have had more strength, you may be sure!"

Then he thinks of the countless days he should have lived, with all the pleasures which he will not have known;—and he, likewise, contemplates the side of the altar.

But the man in the black tunic rushes up to him:

"How scandalous! What? You a victim of election? Think of all those women who are looking at you! And then, God sometimes performs a miracle. Pionius benumbed the hands of his executioners; and the blood of Polycarp extinguished the flames of his funeral-pile."

He turns towards the old man. "Father, father! You ought to edify us by your death. By deferring it, you will, without doubt, commit some bad action which will destroy the fruit of your good deeds. Besides, the power of God is infinite. Perhaps your example will convert the entire people."

And, in the den opposite, the lions stride up and down, without stopping, rapidly, with a continuous movement. The largest of them all at once fixes his eyes on Antony and emits a roar, and a mass of vapour issues from his jaws.

The women are jammed up against the men.

The consoler goes from one to another:

"What would ye say—what would any of you say—if they burned you with plates of iron; if horses tore you asunder; if your body, coated with honey, was devoured by insects? You will have only the death of a hunter who is surprised in a wood."

Antony would much prefer all this than the horrible wild beasts; he imagines he feels their teeth and their talons, and that he hears his back cracking under their jaws.

A belluarius enters the dungeon; the martyrs tremble. One alone amongst them is unmoved—the Phrygian, who has gone into a corner to pray. He had burned three temples. He now advances with lifted arms, open mouth, and his head towards Heaven, without seeing anything, like a somnambulist.

The consoler exclaims:

"Keep back! Keep back! The Spirit of Montanus will destroy ye!"

All fall back, vociferating:

"Damnation to the Montanist!"

They insult him, spit upon him, would like to strike him. The lions, prancing, bite one another's manes. The people yell:

"To the beasts! To the beasts!"

The martyrs, bursting into sobs, catch hold of one another. A cup of narcotic wine is offered to them. They quickly pass it from hand to hand.

Near the door of the den another belluarius awaits the signal. It opens; a lion comes out.

He crosses the arena with great irregular strides. Behind him in a row appear the other lions, then a bear, three panthers, and leopards. They scatter like a flock in a prairie.

The cracking of a whip is heard. The Christians stagger, and, in order to make an end of it, their brethren push them forward.

Antony closes his eyes.

He opens them again. But darkness envelops him. Ere long, it grows bright once more; and he is able to trace the outlines of a plain, arid and covered with knolls, such as may be seen around a deserted quarry. Here and there a clump of shrubs lifts itself in the midst of the slabs, which are on a level with the soil, and above which white forms are bending, more undefined than clouds. Others rapidly make their appearance. Eyes shine through the openings of long veils. By their indolent gait and the perfumes which exhale from them, Antony knows they are ladies of patrician rank. There are also men, but of inferior condition, for they have visages at the same time simple and coarse.

One of the women, with a long breath:

"Ah! how pleasant is the air of the chilly night in the midst of sepulchres! I am so fatigued with the softness of couches, the noise of day, and the oppressiveness of the sun!"

A woman, panting — "Ah! at last, here I am! But how irksome to have wedded an idolater!"

Another — "The visits to the prisons, the conversations with our brethren, all excite the suspicions of our husbands! And we must even hide ourselves from them when making the sign of the Cross; they would take it for a magical conjuration."

Another — "With mine, there was nothing but quarrelling all day long. I did not like to submit to the abuses to which he subjected my person; and, for revenge, he had me persecuted as a Christian."

Another — "Recall to your memory that young man of such striking beauty who was dragged by the heels behind a chariot, like Hector, from the Esquiline Gate to the Mountains of Tibur; and his blood stained the bushes on both sides of the road. I collected the drops — here they are!"

She draws from her bosom a sponge perfectly black, covers it with kisses, and then flings herself upon the slab, crying:

"Ah! my friend! my friend!"

A man — "It is just three years to-day since Domitilla's death. She was stoned at the bottom of the Wood of Proserpine. I gathered her bones, which shone like glow-worms in the grass. The earth now covers them."

He flings himself upon a tombstone.

"O my betrothed! my betrothed!"

And all the others, scattered through the plain:

"O my sister!" "O my brother!" "O my daughter!" "O my mother!"

They are on their knees, their foreheads clasped with their hands, or their bodies lying flat with both arms extended; and the sobs which they repress make their bosoms swell almost to bursting. They gaze up at the sky, saying:

"Have pity on her soul, O my God! She is languishing in the abode of shadows. Deign to admit her into the Resurrection, so that she may rejoice in Thy light!"

Or, with eyes fixed on the flagstones, they murmur:

"Be at rest—suffer no more! I have brought thee wine and meat!"

A widow—"Here is pudding, made by me, according to his taste, with many eggs, and a double measure of flour. We are going to eat together as of yore, is not that so?"

She puts a little of it on her lips, and suddenly begins to laugh in an extravagant fashion, frantically.

The others, like her, nibble a morsel and drink a mouthful; they tell one another the history of their martyrs; their sorrow becomes vehement; their libations increase; their eyes, swimming with tears, are fixed on one another; they stammer with inebriety and desolation. Gradually their hands touch; their lips meet; their veils are torn away, and they embrace one another upon the tombs in the midst of the cups and the torches.

The sky begins to brighten. The mist soaks their garments; and, as if they were strangers to one another, they take their departure by different roads into the country.

The sun shines forth. The grass has grown taller; the plain has become transformed. Across the bamboos, Antony sees a forest of columns of a bluish-grey colour. Those are trunks of trees springing from a single trunk. From each of its branches descend other branches which penetrate into the soil; and the whole of those horizontal and perpendicular lines, indefinitely multiplied, might be compared to a gigantic framework were it not that here and there appears a little fig-tree with a dark foliage like that of a sycamore. Between the branches he distinguishes bunches of yellow flowers and violets, and ferns as large as birds' feathers. Under the lowest branches may be seen at different points the horns of a buffalo, or the glittering eyes of an antelope. Parrots sit perched, butterflies flutter, lizards crawl upon the ground, flies buzz; and one can hear, as it were, in the midst of the silence, the palpitation of an all-permeating life.

At the entrance of the wood, on a kind of pile, is a strange sight — a man coated over with cows' dung, completely naked, more dried-up than a mummy. His joints form knots at the extremities of his bones, which are like sticks. He has clusters of shells in his ears, his face is very long, and his nose is like a vulture's beak. His left arm is held erect in the air, crooked, and stiff as a stake; and he has remained there so long that birds have made a nest in his hair.

At the four corners of his pile four fires are blazing. The sun is right in his face. He gazes at it with great open eyes, and without looking at Antony.

"Brahmin of the banks of the Nile, what sayest thou?"

Flames start out on every side through the partings of the beams; and the gymnosophist resumes:

"Like a rhinoceros, I am plunged in solitude. I dwelt in the tree that was behind me."

In fact, the large fig-tree presents in its flutings a natural excavation of the shape of a man.

"And I fed myself on flowers and fruits with such an observance of precepts that not even a dog has seen me eat.

"As existence proceeds from corruption, corruption from desire, desire from sensation, and sensation from contact, I have avoided every kind of action, every kind of contact, and — without stirring any more than the pillar of a tombstone — exhaling my breath through my two nostrils, fixing my glances upon my nose; and, observing the ether in my spirit, the world in my limbs, the moon in my heart, I pondered on the essence of the great soul, whence continually escape, like sparks of fire, the principles of life. I have, at last, grasped the supreme soul in all beings, all beings in the supreme soul; and I have succeeded in making my soul penetrate the place into which my senses used to penetrate.

"I receive knowledge directly from Heaven, like the bird Tchataka, who quenches his thirst only in the droppings of the rain. From the very fact of my having knowledge of things, things no longer exist. For me now there is no hope and no anguish, no goodness, no virtue, neither day nor night, neither thou nor I—absolutely nothing.

"My frightful austerities have made me superior to the Powers. A contraction of my brain can kill a hundred kings' sons, dethrone gods, overrun the world."

He utters all this in a monotonous voice. The leaves all around him are withered. The rats fly over the ground.

He slowly lowers his eyes towards the flames, which are rising, then adds:

"I have become disgusted with form, disgusted with perception, disgusted even with knowledge itself —for thought does not outlive the transitory fact that gives rise to it; and the spirit, like the rest, is but an illusion.

"Everything that is born will perish; everything that is dead will come to life again. The beings that have actually disappeared will sojourn in wombs not yet formed, and will come back to earth to serve with sorrow other creatures. But, as I have resolved through an infinite number of existences, under the guise of gods, men, and animals, I give up travelling, and no longer wish for this fatigue. I abandon the dirty inn of my body, walled in with flesh, reddened with blood, covered with hideous skin, full of uncleanness; and, for my reward, I shall, finally, sleep in the very depths of the absolute, in annihilation."

The flames rise to his breast, then envelop him. His head stretches across as if through the hole of a wall. His eyes are perpetually fixed in a vacant stare.

Antony gets up again. The torch on the ground has set fire to the splinters of wood, and the flames have singed his beard. Bursting into an exclamation,

Antony tramples on the fire; and, when only a heap of cinders is left:

"Where, then, is Hilarion? He was here just now. I saw him! Ah! no; it is impossible! I am mistaken! How is this? My cell, those stones, the sand, have not, perhaps, any more reality. I must be going mad. Stay! where was I? What was happening here?

"Ah! the gymnosophist! This death is common amongst the Indian sages. Kalanos burned himself before Alexander; another did the same in the time of Augustus. What hatred of life they must have had! —unless, indeed, pride drove them to it. No matter, it is the intrepidity of martyrs! As to the others, I now believe all that has been told me of the excesses they have occasioned.

"And before this? Yes, I recollect! the crowd of heresiarchs . . . What shrieks! what eyes! But why so many outbreaks of the flesh and wanderings of the spirit?

"It is towards God they pretend to direct their thoughts in all these different ways. What right have I to curse them, I who stumble in my own path? When they have disappeared, I shall, perhaps, learn more. This one rushed away too quickly; I had not time to reply to him. Just now it is as if I had in my intellect more space and more light. I am tranquil. I feel myself capable . . . But what is this now? I thought I had extinguished the fire."

A flame flutters between the rocks; and, speedily, a jerky voice makes itself heard from the mountains in the distance.

"Are those the barkings of a hyena, or the lamentations of some lost traveller?"

Antony listens. The flame draws nearer.

And he sees approaching a woman who is weeping, resting on the shoulder of a man with a white
beard. She is covered with a purple garment all in
rags. He, like her, is bare-headed, with a tunic of
the same colour, and carries a bronze vase, whence
arises a small blue flame.

Antony is filled with fear,— and yet he would fain
know who this woman is.

The stranger (Simon)— "This is a young girl, a
poor child, whom I take everywhere with me."

He raises the bronze vase. Antony inspects her
by the light of this flickering flame. She has on her
face marks of bites, and traces of blows along
her arms. Her scattered hair is entangled in the rents
of her rags; her eyes appear insensible to the light.

Simon— "Sometimes she remains thus a long time
without speaking or eating, and utters marvellous
things."

Antony— "Really?"

Simon— "Eunoia! Eunoia! relate what you have
to say!"

She turns around her eyeballs, as if awakening from
a dream, passes her fingers slowly across her two
lids, and in a mournful voice:

Helena (Eunoia)— "I have a recollection of a
distant region, of the colour of emerald. There is
only a single tree there."

Antony gives a start.

"At each step of its huge branches a pair of
spirits stand. The branches around them cross each
other, like the veins of a body, and they watch the
eternal life circulating from the roots, where it is lost

in shadow up to the summit, which reaches beyond the sun. I, on the second branch, illumined with my face the summer nights."

Antony, touching his forehead — "Ah! ah! I understand! the head!"

Simon, with his finger on his lips — "Hush! Hush!"

Helena — "The vessel remained convex: her keel clave the foam. He said to me, 'What does it matter if I disturb my country, if I lose my kingdom! You will be mine, in my own house!'

"How pleasant was the upper chamber of his palace! He would lie down upon the ivory bed, and, smoothing my hair, would sing in an amorous strain. At the end of the day, I could see the two camps and the lanterns which they were lighting; Ulysses at the edge of his tent; Achilles, armed from head to foot, driving a chariot along the seashore."

Antony — "Why, she is quite mad! Wherefore? . . ."

Simon — "Hush! Hush!"

Helena — "They rubbed me with unguents, and sold me to the people to amuse them. One evening, standing with the sistrum in my hand, I was coaxing Greek sailors to dance. The rain, like a cataract, fell upon the tavern, and the cups of hot wine were smoking. A man entered without the door having been opened."

Simon — "It was I! I found you. Here she is, Antony; she who is called Sigeh, Eunoia, Barbelo, Prounikos! The Spirits who govern the world were jealous of her, and they bound her in the body of a woman. She was the Helen of the Trojans, whose memory the poet Stesichorus had rendered infamous. She has been Lucretia, the patrician lady violated by

the kings. She was Delilah, who cut off the hair of
Samson. She was that daughter of Israel who surrendered herself to he-goats. She has loved adultery.
idolatry, lying and folly. She was prostituted by every
nation. She has sung in all the cross-ways. She has
kissed every face. At Tyre, she, the Syrian, was the
mistress of thieves. She drank with them during the
nights, and she concealed assassins amid the vermin
of her tepid bed."

Antony—"Ah! what is coming over me?"

Simon, with a furious air—

"I have redeemed her, I tell you, and re-established
her in all her splendour, such as Caius Cæsar Agricola
became enamoured of when he desired to sleep with
the Moon!"

Antony—"Well! well!"

Simon—"But she really is the Moon! Has not
Pope Clement written that she was imprisoned in a
tower? Three hundred persons came to surround the
tower; and on each of the murderers, at the same
time, the moon was seen to appear,—though there
are not many moons in the world, or many Eunoias!"

Antony—"Yes! . . . I think I recollect . . ."

And he falls into a reverie.

Simon—"Innocent as Christ, who died for men,
she has devoted herself to women. For the power-
lessness of Jehovah is demonstrated by the transgression
of Adam, and we must shake off the old law, opposed,
as it is, to the order of things. I have preached
the new Gospel in Ephraim and in Issachar, along
the torrent of Bizor, behind the lake of Houleh, in the
valley of Mageddo, and beyond the mountains, at
Bostra and at Damas. Let those who are covered
with wine-dregs, those who are covered with dirt,

those who are covered with blood, come to me; and I will wash out their defilement with the Holy Spirit, called by the Greeks, Minerva. She is Minerva! She is the Holy Spirit! I am Jupiter Apollo, the Christ, the Paraclete, the great power of God incarnated in the person of Simon!"

Antony—"Ah! it is you! . . . it is you! But I know your crimes! You were born at Gittha on the borders of Samaria. Dositheus, your first master, dismissed you! You execrate Saint Paul for having converted one of your women; and, vanquished by Saint Peter, in your rage and terror, you flung into the waves the bag which contained your magical instruments!"

Simon—"Do you desire them?"

Antony looks at him, and an inner voice murmurs in his breast, "Why not?"

Simon resumes:

"He who understands the powers of Nature and the substance of spirits ought to perform miracles. It is the dream of all sages—and the desire of which gnaws you; confess it!

"Amongst the Romans I flew so high in the circus that they saw me no more. Nero ordered me to be decapitated; but it was a sheep's head that fell to the ground instead of mine. Finally, they buried me alive; but I came back to life on the third day. The proof of it is that I am here!"

He gives him his hands to smell. They have the odour of a corpse. Antony recoils.

"I can make bronze serpents move, marble statues laugh, and dogs speak. I will show you an immense quantity of gold, I will set up kings, you shall see nations adoring me. I can walk on the clouds and on the waves; pass through mountains; assume the appearance of a young man, or of an old man; of a tiger, or of an ant; take your face, give you mine; and drive the thunderbolt. Do you hear?"

The thunder rolls, followed by flashes of lightning.

"It is the voice of the Most High. 'for the Eternal, thy God, is a fire,' and all creations operate by the emanations of this central fire. You are about to receive the baptism of it—that second baptism, announced by Jesus, which fell on the Apostles one stormy day when the window was open!"

And all the while stirring the flame with his hand, slowly, as if to sprinkle Antony with it:

"Mother of Mercies, thou who discoverest secrets in order that we may have rest in the eighth house . . ."

Antony exclaims:

"Ah! if I had holy water!"

The flame goes out, producing much smoke.

Eunoia and Simon have disappeared.

An extremely cold fog, opaque and fœtid, fills the atmosphere.

Antony, extending his arms like a blind man—

"Where am I? . . . I am afraid of falling into the abyss. And the cross, no doubt, is too far away from me. Ah! what a night! what a night!"

A sudden gust of wind cleaves the fog asunder; and he perceives two men covered with long white tunics. The first is of tall stature, with a sweet expression of countenance and grave deportment. His white hair, parted like that of Christ, descends regularly over his shoulders. He has thrown down a wand which he was carrying in his hand, and which his companion has taken up, making a respectful bow after the fashion of Orientals. The other is small, coarse-looking, flat-nosed, with a thick neck, curly hair, and an air of simplicity. Both of them are barefooted, bare-headed, and covered with dust, like people who have come on a long journey.

Antony, with a start — "What do ye seek? Speak! Go on!"

Damis — He is the little man —

"La, la! . . . worthy hermit! what do you say? I know nothing about it. Here is the Master!"

He sits down; the other remains standing. Silence.

Antony, resumes — "Ye come in this fashion?. . ."

Damis — "Oh! a great distance — a very great distance!"

Antony — "And ye are going? . . ."

Damis, pointing at his companion — "Wherever he wishes."

Antony — "Who, then, is he?"

Damis — "Look at him."

Antony — "He has the appearance of a saint. If I dared . . ."

The fog by this time is quite gone. The atmosphere has become perfectly clear. The moon shines out.

Damis — "What are you thinking of now that you say nothing more?"

Antony — "I am thinking of —— Oh! nothing."

Damis draws close to Apollonius, makes many turns round him, with his figure bent, and without moving his head.

"Master, this is a Galilean hermit who wishes to know the sources of your wisdom."

Apollonius — "Let him approach."

Antony hesitates.

Damis—"Approach!"

Apollonius, in a voice of thunder—

"Approach! You would like to know who I am, what I have done, what I am thinking of? Is that not so, child?"

Antony—" . . . If at the same time those things contribute to my salvation."

Apollonius—"Rejoice! I am about to tell them to you!"

Damis, in a low tone to Antony—

"Is it possible? He must have, at the first glance, recognised your extraordinary inclinations for philosophy! I shall profit by it also myself."

Apollonius—"I will first describe to you the long road I travelled to gain doctrine; and, if you find in all my life one bad action, you will stop me—for he must scandalise by his words who has offended by his actions."

Damis to Antony:

"What a just man! eh?"

Antony—"Decidedly, I believe he is sincere."

Apollonius—"The night of my birth, my mother thought she saw herself gathering flowers on the border of a lake. A flash of lightning appeared; and she brought me into the world amid the cries of swans who were singing in her dream. Up to my fifteenth year, they plunged me three times a day into the fountain Asbadeus, whose waters render perjurers dropsical; and they rubbed my body with leaves of cnyza, to make me chaste. A princess from Palmyra sought me out, one evening, and offered me treasures, which she knew were hidden in tombs. A priest of the temple of Diana cut his throat in despair with the sacrificial knife; and the Governor of Cilicia, after repeated promises, declared before my family that he would put me to death; but it was he who died three days after, assassinated by the Romans."

Damis, to Antony, striking him on the elbow — "Eh? Just as I told you! What a man!"

Apollonius—"I have for four years in succession observed the complete silence of the Pythagoreans. The most unforeseen calamity did not draw one sigh from me; and, at the theatre, when I entered, they turned aside from me as from a phantom."

Damis — "Would you have done that—you?"

Apollonius — "The time of my ordeal ended, I undertook to instruct the priests who had lost the tradition."

Antony — "What tradition?"

Damis — "Let him continue. Be silent!"

Apollonius — "I have conversed with the Samaneans of the Ganges, with the astrologers of Chaldea, with the magi of Babylon, with the Gaulish druids, with the priests of the negroes. I have climbed the fourteen Olympi; I have sounded the Lakes of Sythia; I have measured the vastness of the desert!"

Damis — "All this is undoubtedly true. I was there myself!"

Apollonius — "At first, I went as far as the Hyrcanian Sea. I have gone all round it, and through the country of the Baraomatæ, where Bucephalus is buried. I have gone down to Nineveh. At the gates of the city a man came up to me."

Damis — "I! I! my good Master! I loved you from the very beginning. You were sweeter than a girl, and more beautiful than a god!"

Apollonius, without listening to him — "He wished to accompany me, in order to act as an interpreter for me."

Damis — "But you replied that you understood every language, and that you divined all thoughts. Then I kissed the end of your mantle, and I walked behind you."

Apollonius — "After Ctesiphon, we entered into the land of Babylon."

Damis — "And the satrap uttered an exclamation on seeing a man so pale."

Antony, to himself — "Which signifies —— ?"

Apollonius — "The King received me standing near a throne of silver, in a circular hall studded with stars, and from a cupola hung, from unseen threads, four great golden birds, with both wings extended."

Antony, musing — "Are there such things on the earth?"

Damis — "That is, indeed, a city — Babylon! Everyone is rich there! The houses, painted blue, have gates of bronze, with staircases that lead down to the river."

Making a sketch with his stick on the ground:

"Like that, do you see? And then there are temples, squares, baths, aqueducts! The palaces are covered with copper! and then the interior, if you only saw it!"

Apollonius — "On the northern wall rises a tower, which supports a second, a third, a fourth, a fifth; and there are three others besides! The eighth is a chapel with a bed in it. Nobody enters there but the woman chosen by the priests for the God Belus. The King of Babylon made me take up my quarters in it."

Damis—"They scarcely paid any heed to me. I was left, too, to walk about the streets by myself. I enquired into the customs of the people; I visited the workshops; I examined the huge machines which bring water into the gardens. But it annoyed me to be separated from the Master."

Apollonius—"At last, we left Babylon; and, by the light of the moon, we suddenly saw a wild mare."

Damis—"Yes, indeed! she sprang forth on her iron hoofs; she neighed like an ass; she galloped amongst the rocks. He burst into angry abuse of her; and she disappeared."

Antony, aside—"Where can they have come from?"

Apollonius—"At Taxilla, capital of five thousand fortresses, Phraortes, King of the Ganges, showed us his guard of tall black men, five cubits high, and in the gardens of his palace, under a pavilion of green brocade, an enormous elephant, whom the queens used to amuse themselves in perfuming. This was the elephant of Porus, who fled after the death of Alexander."

Damis—"And which was found again in a forest."

Antony—"They talk a great deal, like drunken people."

Apollonius—"Phraortes made us sit down at his table."

Damis—"What an odd country! The noblemen, while drinking, amuse themselves by flinging arrows under the feet of a child who is dancing. But I do not approve . . ."

Apollonius—"When I was ready to depart, the

King gave me a parasol, and said to me: 'I have, on the Indus, a stud of white camels. When you do not want them any longer, blow into their ears, and they will return.' We proceeded along the river, walking in the night by the gleaming of the glow-worms, who emitted their radiance through the bamboos. The slave whistled an air to keep off the serpents; and our camels bent the reins while passing under the trees, as if under doors that were too low. One day, a black child, who held in his hand a caduceus of gold, conducted us to the College of Sages. Iarchas, their chief, spoke to me of my ancestors, of all my thoughts, of all my actions, and all my existences. He had been the river Indus, and he recalled to my mind that I had conducted the boats on the Nile in the time of King Sesostris."

Damis—"As for me, they told me nothing, so that I do not know what I was."

Antony—"They have the unsubstantial air of shadows."

Apollonius—"We met on the seashore the cynocephali, glutted with milk, who were returning from their expedition in the Island of Taprobane. The tepid waves pushed white pearls before us. The amber cracked under our footsteps. Whales' skeletons were bleaching in the crevices of the cliffs. In short, the earth grew more contracted than a sandal;—and, after casting towards the sun drops from the ocean, we turned to the right to go back. We returned through the region of the Aromatæ, through the country of the Gangaridæ, the promontory of Comaria, the land of the Sachalitæ, of the Aramitæ, and the Homeritæ; then across the Cassanian mountains, the Red Sea, and the Island of Topazes, we penetrated into Ethiopia, through the kingdom of the Pygmæi."

Antony, aside—"How large the earth is!"

Damis—"And when we got home again, all those whom we had known in former days were dead."

Antony hangs his head. Silence.

Apollonius goes on:

"Then they began talking about me in the world. The plague ravaged Ephesus; I made them stone an old mendicant."

Damis—"And the plague was gone!"

Antony—"What! He banishes diseases?"

Apollonius—"At Cnidus, I cured the lover of Venus."

Damis—"Yes, a madman, who had even promised to marry her. To love a woman is bad enough; but a statue—what idiocy! The Master placed his hand on this man's heart, and immediately the love was extinguished."

Antony—"What! He drives out demons?"

Apollonius—"At Tarentum, they brought to the stake a young girl who was dead."

Damis—"The Master touched her lips; and she arose, calling on her mother."

Antony—"Can it be? He brings the dead back to life?"

Apollonius—"I foretold that Vespasian would be Emperor."

Antony—"What! He divines the future?"

Damis—"There was at Corinth——"

Apollonius—"While I was supping with him at the waters of Baia——"

Antony—"Excuse me, strangers; it is late!"

Damis — "—— A young man named Menippus."

Antony — "No! no! go away!"

Apollonius — "—— A dog entered, carrying in its mouth a hand that had been cut off."

Damis — "—— One evening, in one of the suburbs, he met a woman."

Antony — "You do not hear me. Take yourselves off!"

Damis — "—— He prowled vacantly around the couches."

Antony — "Enough!"

Apollonius — "—— They wanted to drive him away."

Damis — "—— Menippus, then, surrendered himself to her; and they became lovers."

Apollonius — "—— And, beating the mosaic floor with his tail, he deposited this hand on the knees of Flavius."

Damis — "—— But, in the morning, at the school-lectures, Menippus was pale."

Antony, with a bound — "Still at it! Well, let them go on, since there is not . . ."

Damis — "The Master said to him: 'O beautiful young man, you are caressing a serpent; and a serpent is caressing you. For how long are these nuptials?' Every one of us went to the wedding."

Antony — "I am doing wrong, surely, in listening to this!"

Damis — "Servants were busily engaged at the vestibule; the doors flew open; nevertheless, one could hear neither the noise of footsteps, nor the sound of opening doors. The Master seated himself beside Menippus. Immediately, the bride was seized with anger against the philosophers. But the vessels of gold, the cup-bearers, the cooks, the attendants, disappeared; the roof flew away; the walls fell in; and Apollonius remained alone, standing with this woman all in tears at his feet. It was a vampire, who satisfied the handsome young men in order to devour their flesh — because nothing is better for phantoms of this kind than the blood of lovers."

Apollonius — "If you wish to know the art——"

Antony — "I wish to know nothing."

Apollonius — "On the evening of our arrival at the gates of Rome——"

Antony — "Oh! yes, tell me about the City of the Popes."

Apollonius — "——A drunken man accosted us who sang with a sweet voice. It was an epithalamium of Nero; and he had the power of causing the death of anyone who heard him with indifference. He carried on his back in a box a string taken from the cithara of the Emperor. I shrugged my shoulders. He threw mud in our faces. Then I unfastened my girdle and placed it in his hands."

Damis — "In this instance you were quite wrong!"

Apollonius — "The Emperor, during the night, made me call at his residence. He played at ossicles with Sporus, leaning with his left arm on a table of agate. He turned round, and, knitting his fair brows: 'Why are you not afraid of me?' he asked. 'Because the God who made you terrible has made me intrepid,' I replied."

Antony, to himself — "Something unaccountable fills me with fear."

Silence.

Damis resumes, in a shrill voice — "All Asia, moreover, could tell you . . . ."

Antony, starting up — "I am sick. Leave me!"

Damis — "Listen now. At Ephesus, he witnessed the death of Domitian, who was at Rome."

Antony, making an effort to laugh — "Is this possible?"

Damis — "Yes, at the theatre, in broad daylight, on the fourteenth of the Kalends of October, he suddenly exclaimed: 'They are murdering Cæsar!' and he added, every now and then, 'He rolls on the ground! Oh! how he struggles! He gets up again; he attempts to fly; the gates are shut. Ah! it is finished. He is dead!' And that very day, in fact, Titus Flavius Domitianus was assassinated, as you are aware."

Antony — "Without the aid of the Devil . . . No doubt . . . ."

Apollonius — "He wished to put me to death, this Domitian. Damis fled by my direction, and I remained alone in my prison."

Damis — "It was a terrible bit of daring, I must confess!"

Apollonius — "About the fifth hour, the soldiers led me to the tribunal. I had my speech quite ready, which I kept under my cloak."

Damis — "The rest of us were on the bank of Puzzoli! We saw you die; we wept; when, towards the sixth hour, all at once, you appeared, and said to us, 'It is I.'"

Antony, aside — "Just like Him!"

Damis, very loudly — "Absolutely!"

Antony — "Oh, no! you are lying, are you not? You are lying!"

Apollonius — "He came down from Heaven — I ascend there, thanks to my virtue, which has raised me even to the height of the Most High!"

Damis — "Tyana, his native city, has erected a temple with priests in his honour!"

Apollonius draws close to Antony, and, bending towards his ear, says:

"The truth is, I know all the gods, all the rites, all the prayers, all the oracles. I have penetrated into the cavern of Trophonius, the son of Apollo. I have moulded for the Syracusans the cakes which they use on the mountains. I have undergone the eighty tests of Mithra. I have pressed against my heart the serpent of Sabacius. I have received the scarf of the Cabiri. I have bathed Cybele in the waves of the Campanian Gulf; and I have passed three moons in the caverns of Samothrace!"

Damis, laughing stupidly — "Ah! ah! ah! at the mysteries of the Bona Dea!"

Apollonius — "And now we are renewing our pilgrimage. We are going to the North, the side of the swans and the snows. On the white plain the blind hippopodes break with the ends of their feet the ultramarine plant."

Damis — "Come! it is morning! The cock has crowed; the horse has neighed; the ship is ready."

Antony — "The cock has not crowed. I hear the cricket in the sands, and I see the moon, which remains in its place."

Apollonius — "We are going to the South, behind the mountains and the huge waves, to seek in the perfumes for the cause of love. You shall inhale the odour of myrrhodion, which makes the weak die. You shall bathe your body in the lake of pink oil of the Island of Juno. You shall see sleeping under the primroses the lizard who awakens all the centuries when at his maturity the carbuncle falls from his forehead. The stars glitter like eyes, the cascades sing like lyres, an intoxicating fragrance arises from the opening flowers. Your spirit shall expand in this atmosphere, and it will show itself in your heart as well as in your face."

Damis — "Master, it is time! The wind is about to rise; the swallows are awakening; the myrtle-leaf is shed."

Apollonius — "Yes, let us go!"

Antony — "No — not I! I remain!"

Apollonius — "Do you wish me to show you the plant Balis, which resuscitates the dead?"

Damis — "Ask him rather for the bloodstone, which attracts silver, iron and bronze!"

Antony — "Oh! how sick I feel! how sick I feel!"

Damis — "You shall understand the voices of all creatures, the roarings, the cooings!"

Apollonius — "I will make you mount the unicorns, the dragons, and the dolphins!"

Antony, weeps — "Oh! oh! oh!"

Apollonius — "You shall know the demons who dwell in the caverns, those who speak in the woods, those who move about in the waves, those who drive the clouds."

Damis — "Fasten your girdle! tie your sandals!"

Apollonius — "I will explain to you the reasons for the shapes of divinities; why it is that Apollo is upright, Jupiter sitting down, Venus black at Corinth, square at Athens, conical at Paphos."

Antony, clasping his hands — "I wish they would go away! I wish they would go away!"

Apollonius — "I will snatch off before your eyes the armour of the Gods; we shall force the sanctuaries; I will make you violate the pythoness!"

Antony — "Help, Lord!"

He flings himself against the cross.

Apollonius — "What is your desire? your dream? There is barely time to think of it . . ."

Antony — "Jesus, Jesus, come to my aid!"

Apollonius — "Do you wish me to make Jesus appear?"

Antony — "What? How?"

Apollonius — "It shall be He — and no other! He shall cast off His crown, and we shall speak together face to face!"

Damis, in a low tone — "Say what you wish for most! Say what you wish for most!"

Antony, at the foot of the cross, murmurs prayers. Damis continues to run around him with wheedling gestures.

"See, worthy hermit, dear Saint Antony! pure man, illustrious man! man who cannot be sufficiently praised! Do not be alarmed; this is an exaggerated style of speaking, borrowed from the Orientals. It in no way prevents——"

Apollonius — "Let him alone, Damis! He believes, like a brute, in the reality of things. The fear which he has of the gods prevents him from comprehending them; and he eats his own words, just like a jealous king! But you, my son, quit me not!"

He steps back to the verge of the cliffs, passes over it and remains there, hanging in mid-air:

"Above all forms, farther than the earth, beyond the skies, dwells the World of Ideas, entirely filled with the Word. With one bound we leap across

Space, and you shall grasp in its infinity the Eternal, the Absolute Being! Come! give me your hand. Let us go!"

The pair, side by side, rise softly into the air.

Antony, embracing the cross, watches them ascending.

They disappear.

CHAPTER V.

ALL GODS, ALL RELIGIONS.

ANTONY, walking slowly—"That was really Hell!

"Nebuchadnezzar did not dazzle me so much. The Queen of Sheba did not bewitch me so thoroughly. The way in which he spoke about the gods filled me with a longing to know them.

"I recollect having seen hundreds of them at a time, in the Island of Elephantinum, in the reign of Dioclesian. The Emperor had given up to the nomads a large territory, on condition that they should protect the frontiers; and the treaty was concluded in the name of the invisible Powers. For the gods of every people were ignorant about other people. The Barbarians had brought forward theirs. They occupied the hillocks of sand which line the river. One could see them holding their idols between their arms, like great paralytic children, or else, sailing amid cataracts on trunks of palm-trees, they pointed out from a distance the amulets on their necks and the tattooings on their breasts; and that is not more criminal than the religion of the Greeks, the Asiatics, and the Romans.

"When I dwelt in the Temple of Heliopolis, I used often to contemplate all the objects on the walls: vultures carrying sceptres, crocodiles playing on lyres, men's faces joined to serpents' bodies, women with cows' heads prostrated before the ithyphallic deities; and their supernatural forms carried me away into other worlds. I wished to know what those calm eyes were gazing at. In order that matter should have so much power, it should contain a spirit. The souls of the gods are attached to their images. Those who possess external beauty may fascinate us; but the others, who are abject or terrible . . . how to believe in them? . . ."

And he sees moving past, close to the ground, leaves, stones, shells, branches of trees, vague representations of animals, then a species of dropsical dwarfs. These are gods. He bursts out laughing.

Behind him, he hears another outburst of laughter; and Hilarion presents himself, dressed like a hermit, much bigger than before — in fact, colossal.

Antony is not surprised at seeing him again.

"What a brute one must be to adore a thing like that!"

Hilarion — "Oh! yes; very much of a brute!"

Then advance before them, one by one, idols of all nations and all ages, in wood, in metal, in granite, in feathers, and in skins sewn together. The oldest of them, anterior to the Deluge, are lost to view beneath the seaweed which hangs from them like hair. Some, too long for their lower portions, crack in their joints and break their loins while walking. Others allow sand to flow out through holes in their bellies.

Antony and Hilarion are prodigiously amused. They hold their sides from sheer laughter.

After this, idols pass with faces like sheep. They stagger on their bandy legs, open wide their eyelids, and bleat out, like dumb animals: "Ba! ba! ba!"

In proportion as they approach the human type, they irritate Antony the more. He strikes them with his fist, kicks them, rushes madly upon them. They begin to present a horrible aspect, with high tufts, eyes like bulls, arms terminated with claws, and the jaws of a shark. And, before these gods, men are slaughtered on altars of stone, while others are pounded in vats, crushed under chariot-wheels, or nailed to trees. There is one of them, all in red-hot iron, with the horns of a bull, who devours children.

Antony — "Horror!"

Hilarion — "But the gods always demand sufferings. Your own, even, has wished——"

Antony, weeping — "Say no more — hold your tongue!"

The enclosure of rocks changes into a valley. A herd of oxen pastures there on the shorn grass. The shepherd who has charge of them perceives a cloud; and in a sharp voice pierces the air with words of urgent entreaty.

Hilarion — "As he wants rain, he tries, by his strains, to coerce the King of Heaven to open the fruitful cloud."

Antony, laughing — "This is too silly a form of presumption!"

Hilarion — "Why, then, do you perform exorcisms?"

The valley becomes a sea of milk, motionless and illimitable.

In the midst of it floats a long cradle, formed by the coils of a serpent, all whose heads, bending forward at the same time, overshadow a god who lies there asleep. He is young, beardless, more beautiful than a girl, and covered with diaphanous veils. The pearls of his tiara shine softly, like moons; a chaplet of stars winds itself many times above his breast, and, with one hand under his head and the other arm extended, he reposes with a dreamy and intoxicated air. A woman squatted before his feet awaits his awakening.

Hilarion — "This is the primordial duality of the Brahmans — the absolute not expressing itself by any form."

Upon the navel of the god a stalk of lotus has grown; and in its calyx appears another god with three faces.

Antony — "Hold! what an invention!"

Hilarion — "Father, Son and Holy Ghost, in the same way make only one person!"

The three heads are turned aside, and three immense gods appear. The first, who is of a rosy hue, bites the end of his toe. The second, who is blue, tosses four arms about. The third, who is green, weaves a necklace of human skulls. Immediately in front of them rise three goddesses, one wrapped in a net, another offering a cup, and the third brandishing a bow.

And these gods, these goddesses multiply, become tenfold. On their shoulders rise arms, and at the ends of their arms are hands holding banners, axes, bucklers, swords, parasols and drums. Fountains spring from their heads, grass hangs from their nostrils.

Riding on birds, cradled on palanquins, throned on seats of gold, standing in niches of ivory, they dream,

travel, command, drink wine and inhale flowers.
Dancing-girls whirl around; giants pursue monsters; at
the entrances to the grottoes, solitaries meditate.
Myriads of stars and clouds of streamers mingle in an
indistinguishable throng. Peacocks drink from the
streams of golden dust. The embroidery of the pa-
vilions blends with the spots of the leopards. Coloured rays cross one another in the blue air, amid
the flying of arrows and the swinging of censers.
And all this unfolds itself, like a lofty frieze, leaning
with its base on the rocks and mounting to the very
sky.

Antony, dazzled — "What a number of them there
are! What do they wish?"

Hilarion — "The one who is scratching his abdomen with his elephant's trunk is the solar god, the
inspirer of wisdom. That other, whose six heads
carry towers and fourteen handles of javelins, is the
prince of armies, the fire-devourer. The old man
riding on a crocodile is going to bathe the souls of
the dead on the seashore. They will be tormented
by this black woman with rotten teeth, the govern-
ess of hell. The chariot drawn by red mares,
which a legless coachman is driving, is carrying
about in broad daylight the master of the sun. The
moon-god accompanies him in a litter drawn by
three gazelles. On her knees, on the back of a par-
rot, the goddess of beauty is presenting her round
breast to Love, her son. Here she is farther on;
she leaps with joy in the prairies. Look! look!
With a radiant mitre on her head, she runs over the
cornfields, over the waves, mounts into the air, and
exhibits herself everywhere. Between these gods sit
the genii of the winds, of the planets, of the months.

of the days, and a hundred thousand others! And their aspects are multiplied, their transformations rapid. Here is one who from a fish has become a tortoise, he assumes the head of a wild boar, the stature of a dwarf!"

Antony—"For what purpose?"

Hilarion—"To establish equilibrium, to combat evil. Life is exhausted, its forms are used up; and it is necessary to progress by metamorphoses of them."

Suddenly a naked man appears, seated in the middle of the sand with his legs crossed. A large circle vibrates, suspended behind him. The little curls of his black hair, deepening into an azure tint, twist symmetrically around a protuberance at the top of his head. His arms, of great length, fall straight down his sides. His two hands, with open palms, rest evenly on his thighs. The lower portions of his feet present the figures of two suns; and he remains completely motionless in front of Antony and Hilarion, with all the gods around him placed at intervals upon the rocks, as if on the seats of a circus. His lips open, and in a deep voice he says:

"I am the master of the great charity, the help of creatures, and I expound the law to believers and to the profane alike. To save the world I wished to be born amongst men; the gods wept when I went away. At first, I sought a woman suitable for the purpose—of warlike race, the spouse of a king, exceedingly virtuous and beautiful, with a deep navel, a body firm as a diamond; and at the time of the full moon, without the intervention of any male, I entered her womb. I came out through her right side. Then the stars stopped in their motions."

Hilarion murmurs between his teeth:

"'And when they saw the stars stop, they conceived a great joy!'"

Antony looks more attentively at the Buddha, who resumes:

"From the bottom of the Himalaya, a religious centenarian set forth to see me."

Hilarion — "'A man called Simeon, who was not to die before he had seen the Christ!'"

The Buddha — "They brought me to the schools. I knew more than the doctors."

Hilarion — " . . . 'In the midst of the doctors; and all those who heard him were ravished by his wisdom.'"

Antony makes a sign to Hilarion to keep silent.

The Buddha — "I went continually to meditate in the gardens. The shadows of the trees used to move; but the shadow of the one that sheltered me did not move. No one could equal me in the knowledge of the Sacred Writings, the enumeration of atoms, the management of elephants, waxworks, astronomy, poetry, boxing, all exercises and all arts. In compliance with custom, I took a wife; and I passed the days in my royal palace, arrayed in pearls, under a shower of perfumes, fanned by the fly-flappers of thirty-three thousand women, and gazing at my people from the tops of my terraces adorned with resounding bells. But the sight of the world's miseries made me turn aside from pleasures. I fled. I went a-begging on high-ways, covered with rags collected in the sepulchres; and, as there was a very learned hermit, I offered myself as his servant. I guarded his door; I washed his feet. All sensation, all joy, all languor, were annihilated. Then, concentrating my thoughts on a larger field of meditation, I came to know the essence of things, the illusion of forms. I speedily abandoned the science of the Brakhmans. They are eaten up with lusts beneath their austere exterior; they anoint themselves with filth, and sleep upon thorns, believing that they arrive at happiness through the path of death!"

Hilarion — "Pharisees, hypocrites, whited sepulchres, race of vipers!"

The Buddha "I, too, have done astonishing things —eating for a day only a single grain of rice—and at that time grains of rice were not bigger than they are now—my hair fell off; my body became black; my eyes, sunken in their sockets, seemed like stars seen at the bottom of a well. For six years I never moved, remaining exposed to flies, to lions, and to serpents; and I subjected myself to burning suns, heavy showers, snow, lightning, hail, and tempest, without even shielding myself with my hand. The travellers who passed, assuming that I was dead, flung clods of earth at me from a distance.

"There only remained for me to be tempted by the Devil.

"I invoked him.

"His sons came—hideous, covered with scales, nauseous as charcoal, howling, hissing, bellowing, flinging at each other armour and dead men's bones. Some of them spirted out flames through their nostrils; others spread around darkness with their wings; others carried chaplets of fingers that had been cut off; others drank the venom of serpents out of the hollows of their hands. They have the heads of pigs, rhinoceroses, or toads—all kinds of figures calculated to inspire respect or terror."

Antony, aside—"I endured that myself in former times."

The Buddha—"Then he sent me his daughters—beautiful, well-attired with golden girdles, teeth white as the jasmine, and limbs round as an elephant's trunk. Some of them stretched up their arms when they yawned to display the dimples in their elbows; others blinked their eyes; others began to laugh and others unfastened one another's garments. Amongst them were blushing virgins, matrons full of pride, and queens with great trains of baggage and attendants."

Antony, aside—"Ah! that also!"

The Buddha—"Having vanquished the demon. I passed twelve years in nourishing myself exclusively on perfumes,—and, as I had acquired the five virtues, the five faculties, the ten forces, the eighteen substances and penetrated into the four spheres of the invisible world, the Intelligence was mine, and I became the Buddha!"

All the gods bow down, those who have many heads lower them all at the same time. He raises his hand on high in the air, and resumes:

"In view of the deliverance of beings, I have made hundreds of thousands of sacrifices; I have given to the poor robes of silk, beds, chariots, houses, heaps of gold and diamonds. I have given my hands to the one-handed, my legs to the lame, my eyes to the blind; I have cut off my head for the decapitated. At the time when I was king, I distributed the provinces; at the time when I was Brakhman, I despised nobody. When I was a solitary I spoke words of tenderness to the thief who tried to cut my throat. When I was a tiger, I let myself die of hunger. And in this final stage of existence, having preached the

7—8

law, I have nothing more to do. The great period is accomplished. The men, the animals, the gods, the bamboos, the oceans, the mountains, the grains of sand of the Ganges, with the myriads of myriads of stars, everything, must perish; and, until the new births, a flame will dance on the ruins of a world's overthrow."

Then a vertigo seizes the gods. They stagger, fall into convulsions, and vomit forth their existences. Their crowns break to pieces; their standards fly away. They get rid of their attributes and their sexes, fling over their shoulders the cups from which they drink immortality, strangle themselves with their serpents, and vanish in smoke; and, when they have all disappeared:

Hilarion, slowly — "You have just seen the creed of many hundreds of millions of men! "

Antony is on the earth, his face in his hands. Standing close to him, and turning his back to the cross, Hilarion watches him.

A rather lengthened period elapses.

Then a singular being appears, with the head of a man and the body of a fish. He advances straight through the air, tossing the sand with his tail; and his patriarchal face and his little arms make Antony laugh.

Oannes, in a plaintive voice — "Treat me with respect! I am the contemporary of the beginning of things.

"I have dwelt in the shapeless world, where slumbered hermaphrodite animals, under the weight of an opaque atmosphere, in the depths of gloomy waves — when the fingers, the fins, and the wings were confounded, and eyes without heads floated like molluscs amongst human-faced bulls and dog-footed serpents.

"Over the whole of those beings Omoroca, bent like a hoop, stretched her woman's body. But Belus cut her clean in two halves, made the earth with one, and the heavens with another; and the two worlds alike mutually contemplate each other. I, the first consciousness of chaos, I have arisen from the abyss to harden matter, to regulate forms; and I have taught men fishing, the sowing of seed, the scripture, and the history of the gods. Since then, I live in the ponds that remained after the Deluge. But the desert grows larger around them; the wind flings sand into them; the sun consumes them; and I expire on my bed of lemon while gazing across the water at the stars. Thither am I returning."

He makes a plunge and disappears in the Nile.

Hilarion — "This is an ancient god of the Chaldeans!"

Antony, ironically — "Who, then, were the gods of Babylon?"

Hilarion — "You can see them!"

And they find themselves upon the platform of a quadrangular tower rising above other towers, which, growing narrower in proportion as they rise, form a monstrous pyramid. You may distinguish below a great, black mass — the city, without doubt — stretching along the plain. The air is cold; the sky is of a sombre blue; the multitudinous stars palpitate.

In the middle of the platform stands a column of white stone. Priests in linen robes pass and return all round, so as to describe in their evolutions a moving circle, and, with heads raised, they contemplate the stars.

Hilarion points out several of them to Saint Antony:

"There are thirty chief priests. Fifteen gaze upon the region above the earth, and fifteen on the region below it. At regular intervals one of them rushes from the upper regions to the lower, whilst another abandons the lower to mount towards the empyrean.

"Of the seven planets, two are benevolent, two malevolent, and three ambiguous; everything in the world depends on these eternal fires. According to their position and their movements, one may draw prognostications, and you are now treading on the most sacred spot on earth. There Pythagoras and Zoroaster may be met. Two thousand years have these men been observing the sky, the better to comprehend the gods."

Antony — "The stars are not gods!"

Hilarion — "Yes! say they; for, while things are continually passing around us, the sky, like eternity, remains unchangeable!"

Antony — "Nevertheless, it has a master."

Hilarion, pointing at the column — "That is Belus, the first ray, the sun, the male!—the other, which is fruitful, is under him!"

Antony observes a garden lighted up with lamps. He is in the midst of the crowd in an avenue of cypress-trees. To right and left little paths lead towards huts erected in a wood of pomegranate-trees, which protect lattices of reeds. The men, for the most part, have pointed caps with laced robes, like the plumage of peacocks. There are people from the North clad in bearskins; nomads in brown woollen cloaks; pale Gangarides with long ear-rings; and the classes, like the nationalities, appear to be confused, for sailors and stone-cutters jostle against princes wearing tiaras of carbuncles and carrying large walking-sticks with carved heads. All hurry forward with dilated nostrils, filled with the same desire.

From time to time they got out of the way, in order to allow a long, covered chariot, drawn by oxen, to pass, or perhaps it is an ass jolting on his back a woman closely veiled, who also disappears in the direction of the huts.

Antony is frightened. He desires to turn back. However, an inexpressible curiosity leads him on.

Beneath the cypress-trees women are squatted in rows upon deerskins, each of them having for a diadem a plait of cords. Some of them, magnificently attired, address the passers-by in loud tones. The more timid keep their features hidden between their hands, whilst, from behind, a matron—no doubt, their mother—encourages them. Others, with heads enveloped in black shawls, and the rest of their bodies quite nude, seem, at a distance, like statues of flesh. As soon as a man flings money on their knees, they rise. And one can hear kisses amid the foliage, and sometimes a great, bitter cry.

Hilarion—"Those are the virgins of Babylon who prostitute themselves to the goddess."

Antony—"What goddess?"

Hilarion—"There she is!"

And he shows Antony, at the very end of the avenue, on the threshold of an illuminated grotto, a block of stone representing a woman.

Antony—"Infamy! What an abomination to give a sex to God!"

Hilarion—"You conceive Him, surely, as a living person!"

Once more Antony finds himself in darkness.

He perceives in the air a luminous circle placed on horizontal wings. This species of ring surrounds, like a girdle that is too loose, the figure of a small man with a mitre on his head and a crown in his hand, the lower part of whose body is shut out from view by the huge feathers exhibited in his kilt.

This is Ormuz, the God of the Persians. He flutters while he exclaims:

"I am terrified! I catch a glimpse of his mouth. I have vanquished thee, Ahriman! But thou art beginning again!

"At first, revolting against me, thou didst destroy the eldest of creatures, Kaiomortz, the man-bull. Then, thou didst seduce the first human pair, Meschia and Meschiana, and didst fill their hearts with darkness, and press forward thy battalions towards Heaven.

"I had my own, the inhabitants of the stars, and I gazed down from my throne on all the planets in their different spheres.

"Mithra, my son, dwelt in an inaccessible spot. There he received souls, and sent them forth, and, each morning he arose to pour out his riches.

"The splendour of the firmament was reflected by the earth. The fire shone on the mountains — image of the other fire with which I have created all beings. To secure it from defilement, they did not burn the dead, who were transported to Heaven on the beaks of birds.

"I have regulated pasturages, labours, the wood of sacrifice, the forms of cups, the words that must be uttered in insomnia; and my priests prayed continually in order that their worship should correspond to the eternity of God. They purified themselves with water; they offered up loaves on the altars; they confessed their sins in loud tones.

"Homa gave himself to men to drink in order to communicate his strength to them.

"While the genii of Heaven were fighting the demons, the children of Iran chased the serpents. The King, whom a countless train of courtiers served on bended knees, was attired so as to resemble me in person, and wore my head-dress. His gardens had the magnificence of a celestial earth; and his tomb represented him slaying a monster—emblem of the good which exterminates evil. For, one day, it came to pass—thanks to the endless course of time—that I triumphed over Ahriman. But the interval that separates us is disappearing; the night is rising! Help, Amschaspands, Irzeds, Ferouers! Come to my assistance, Mithra! take thy sword! Caosyac, who must come back to save the world, defend me! How is this? . . . No one!

"Ah! I am dying! Ahriman, thou art the master!"

Hilarion, behind Antony, restrains an exclamation of joy, and Ormuz plunges into the darkness.

Then appears the great Diana of Ephesus, black, with enamelled eyes, elbows at her sides, forearms turned out, and hands open.

Lions crouch upon her shoulders; fruits, flowers and stars cross one another upon her chest; further down three rows of breasts exhibit themselves, and from the belly to the feet she is caught in a close sheath, from which sprout forth, in the centre of her body, bulls, stags, griffins and bees. She is seen in the white gleaming caused by a disc of silver, round as the full moon, placed behind her head.

"Where is my temple? Where are my amazons? How is it with me — me, the incorruptible — that I find myself so impotent?"

Her flowers wither; her fruits, over-ripe, hang loose; the lions and the bulls bow down their necks; the stags, exhausted, begin to pant; the bees, with a faint buzzing, fall dying upon the ground. She presses her breasts one after the other. They are empty! But, yielding to a desperate pressure, her sheath bursts open. She clutches the end of it, like the skirt of a dress, flings into it her animals and her flower-wreaths, then goes back into the darkness; and in the distance voices murmur, grumble, roar, cry, or bellow. The density of the night is increased by the winds. A warm shower begins to fall in heavy drops.

Antony — "How pleasant is this odour of palm-trees, this rustling of green leaves, this transparency of fountains! I would like to lie down flat upon the ground, in order to feel it close to my heart, and my life would be renewed in eternal youth!"

He hears the sound of castanets and cymbals, and, in the midst of a rustic crowd, men clad in white tunics, with red bands, lead out an ass, richly harnessed, his tail adorned with ribands and his hoofs painted. A box, covered with a saddle-cloth of yellow linen, sways to and fro upon his back, between two baskets, one of which receives the offerings deposited there — eggs, grapes, pears, cheeses, poultry, and small coins — while the second is full of roses, which the drivers of the ass scatter before him as they move along. The latter wear pendants in their ears, large cloaks, plaited tresses, and have their cheeks painted. Each of them has an olive crown fastened around his forehead by a figured medallion. They carry daggers in their girdles, and flourish whips with ebony handles, each having three thongs mounted with ossicles. The last in the procession fix in the ground erect, as a chandelier, a huge pine-tree, whose summit is on fire, and the lowest branches of which overshadow a little sheep.

The ass stops. The saddle-cloth is removed; and underneath appears a second covering of black felt. Then one of the men in a white tunic begins to dance, while playing upon castanets; while another, on his knees before the box, beats a tambourine; and the oldest of the band commences:

·'Here is the Bona Dea, the divinity of the mountains, the great mother of Syria! Draw hither, honest people! She procures joy, heals the sick, bestows fortunes, and satisfies lovers. It is we who bring her out to walk in the country in fine weather and bad weather. We often sleep in the open air, and we have not a well-served table every day. The thieves dwell in the woods. The beasts rush forth from their dens. Slippery paths line the precipices. Look here! look here!"

They raise the coverlet and disclose a box incrusted with little pebbles.

"Higher than the cedar-trees she hovers in the blue ether. More circumambient than the winds, she surrounds the world. Her respiration is exhaled through the nostrils of tigers; her voice growls beneath the volcanoes; her anger is the storm; and the pallor of her face has made the moon white. She ripens the harvests; she swells out the rinds; she makes the beard grow. Give her something, for she hates the avaricious!"

The box flies open; and beneath an awning of blue silk is seen a little image of Cybele, glittering with spangles, crowned with towers, and seated on a chariot of red stone, drawn by two lions with raised paws.

The crowd presses forward to see.

The archi-gallus continues:

"She loves the sounds of dulcimers, the stamping of feet, the howling of wolves, the echoing mountains and the deep gorges, the flower of the almond-tree, the pomegranate and the green figs, the whirling dance, the high-sounding flute, the sweet sap, the salt tear,—blood! Help! help! Mother of mountains!"

They flagellate themselves with their whips, and the strokes resound on their breasts. The skins of the tambourines vibrate till they almost burst. They seize their knives and inflict gashes on their arms:

"She is sad: let us be sad! He who is doomed to suffer must weep! In that way your sins will be remitted. Blood washes out everything: shed drops of it around, then, like flowers. She demands that of another — of one who is pure!"

The archi-gallus raises his knife above the sheep,

Antony, seized with horror—"Don't slaughter the lamb!"

A purple flood gushes forth. The priests sprinkle the crowd with it; and all—including Antony and Hilarion—ranged around the burning tree, silently watch the last palpitations of the victim. From the midst of the priests comes a woman, exactly like the image enclosed in the little box. She stops on seeing a young man in a Phrygian cap.

His thighs are covered with tight-fitting breeches opened here and there by lozenges which are fastened with coloured bows. He rests his elbows against one of the branches of the tree, holding a flute in his hand, in a languishing attitude.

Cybele, encircling his figure with her arms —

"To rejoin thee I have travelled through every region — and famine ravaged the fields. Thou hast deceived me! No matter, — I love thee! Warm my body! Let us unite!"

Atys — "The spring-time will return no more, O eternal Mother! Despite my love, it is not possible to penetrate thy essence. I should like to cover myself with a coloured robe like thine. I envy thy breasts, swollen with milk, the length of thy tresses, thy mighty sides from which spring living creatures. Would that I were like thee! Would that I were woman! But no! that can never be! My virility fills me with horror!"

With a sharp stone he mutilates himself; then he begins to run madly around.

The priests imitate the god; the faithful, the priests. Men and women exchange their garments and embrace one another; and this whirlwind of blood-stained flesh hurries away, whilst the voices, ever continuing, become more clamorous and shrill, like those one hears at funerals.

A great catafalque hung with purple carries on its summit a bed of ebony, surrounded by torches and baskets of silver filigree, in which are contained green lettuces, mallows, and fennel. Upon the seats, above and below, are seated women, all attired in black, with girdles undone and naked feet, and holding with a melancholy air huge bouquets of flowers.

On the ground, at the corners the platform, alabaster urns filled with myrrh are sending up light wreaths of smoke. On the bed may be seen the corpse of a man. Blood trickles from his thigh. His arm is hanging down, and a dog, who is howling, licks his nails. The line of torches placed too close to one another prevents his figure from being completely visible. Antony is seized with anguish. He is afraid of seeing the face of some one he knew.

The women cease their sobbing; and, after an interval of silence, all, at the same time, burst into a psalm:

"Beautiful! beautiful! he is beautiful! Enough of sleep—raise his head! Up! Inhale our bouquets! These are narcissi and anemones gathered in thy gardens to please thee. Return to life! thou fillest us with fear!

"Speak! What dost thou require? Dost thou wish to drink wine? Dost thou wish to sleep in our beds? Dost thou wish to eat the honey-cakes which have the form of little birds?

"Let us press close to his hips! let us kiss his breast! Hold! hold! feel thou our fingers covered with rings which are stealing over thy body, and our lips which are seeking thy mouth, and our hair which is sweeping thy legs, insensible god, deaf to our prayers!"

They burst into shrieks, tearing their faces with their nails, then become silent; and only the howling of the dog is heard.

"Alas! alas! The dark blood rushes over his snowy flesh. See how his knees writhe, how his sides give way! The flowers upon his face have soaked the gore. He is dead! Let us weep! let us lament!"

They come all in a row to fling down between the torches their flowing locks, resembling at a distance black or yellow serpents; and the catafalque is softly lowered to the level of a cave — a gloomy sepulchre, which is yawning in the background.

Then a woman bends over the corpse. Her hair, which never has been cut, covers her from head to foot. She sheds so many tears that her grief does not seem to be like that of others, but superhuman, infinite.

Antony thinks of the mother of Jesus.

She says:

"Thou didst escape from the East, and thou didst press me in thy arms all quivering with dew, O sun! Doves fluttered above the azure of thy mantle, our kisses caused breezes amid the foliage, and I abandoned myself to thy love, delighting in the exquisite sensation of my own weakness.

"Alas! alas! Why art thou about to rush away over the mountains? At the autumnal equinox a wild boar wounded thee! Thou art dead, and the fountains weep and the trees droop, and the winter wind is whistling through the leafless branches.

"My eyes are about to close, seeing that darkness is covering thee. By this time thou art dwelling on the other side of the world, near my more powerful rival.

"O Persephone, all that is beautiful goes down to thee and returns no more!"

While she has been speaking, her companions have taken the dead body to lower it into the sepulchre. It remains in their hands. It was only a corpse of wax!

Antony experiences a kind of relief. The whole scene vanishes, and the cell, the rocks, and the cross reappear! And now he distinguishes on the other side of the Nile a woman standing in the middle of the desert. She holds with her hand the end of a long black veil, which conceals her figure; while she carries on her left arm a little child, which she is suckling. At her side a huge ape is squatted on the sand. She lifts her head towards the sky, and, in spite of the distance, her voice can be heard.

Isis—"O Neith, beginning of things! Ammon, lord of eternity! Ptha, demiurgus! Thoth, his intelligence! Gods of Amenthi! Special Triads of the Nomes! Sparrow-hawks in the azure! Sphinxes on the outsides of temples! Ibises standing between the horns of oxen! Planets! Constellations! River-banks! Murmurs of wind! Reflections of light! Tell me where to find Osiris!

"I have sought for him through all the water-courses and all the lakes, and, farther still, in the Phœnician Byblos. Anubis, with ears erect, jumped round me, barking, and with his nose scenting out the clumps of tamarind. Thanks, good Cynocephalus, thanks!"

She gives the ape two or three friendly little slaps on the head.

"The hideous red-haired Typhon killed him and tore him to pieces. We have found all his members. But I have not got that which made me fruitful!"

She utters bitter lamentations.

Antony is seized with rage. He casts pebbles at her insultingly:

"Impure one! begone, begone!"

Hilarion—"Respect her! This is the religion of your ancestors! You have worn her amulets in your cradle!"

Isis—"In former times, when the summer returned, the inundation drove to the desert the impure beasts. The dykes flew open; the boats dashed against one another; the panting earth drank the stream till it was glutted. O god! with horns of bull, thou didst stretch thyself upon my breast, and the lowing of the eternal cow was heard!

"The new-sown crops, the harvests, the thrashing of corn, and the vintages succeeded each other regularly in unison with the changes of the seasons. In the nights, ever clear, the great stars shed forth their beams. The days were steeped in an unchanging splendour. The sun and the moon were seen like a royal pair on either side of the horizon.

"We were enthroned in a world more sublime— twin monarchs, spouses from the bosom of eternity; he holding a sceptre with the head of a conchoupha, and I a sceptre with a lotus-flower, we stood with hands joined;—and the crash of empires did not change our attitude.

"Egypt lay stretched beneath us, monumental and solemn, long, like the corridor of a temple, with obelisks at the right, pyramids at the left, its labyrinth in the middle; and everywhere avenues of monsters, forests of columns, massive archways flanking gates which have for their summit the earth's sphere between two wings.

"The animals of her zodiac found their counterparts in her plains, and with their forms and colours filled her mysterious writings. Divided into twelve regions, as the year is into twelve months— each month, each day, having its god—she reproduced the immutable order of the heavens; and man, though he died, did not lose his lineaments, but, saturated with perfumes and becoming imperishable, he went to sleep for three thousand years in a silent Egypt.

"The latter, greater than the other, spread out beneath the earth. Thither one descended by means of staircases leading to halls where were reproduced the joys of the good, the tortures of the wicked, everything that takes place in the third invisible world. Ranged along the walls, the dead, in painted coffins, awaited each their turn; and the soul, free from migrations, continued its sleep till it awakened in another life.

"Meanwhile, Osiris sometimes came back to see me. His shade made me the mother of Harpocrates."

She gazes on the child:

"It is he! Those are his eyes; those are his tresses, curling like a ram's horns. Thou shalt begin his works over again. We shall bloom afresh, like the lotus. I am always the great Isis! Nobody has ever yet lifted my veil! My offspring is the sun!

"Sun of spring, let the clouds obscure thy face! The breath of Typhon devours the pyramids. Just now I have seen the Sphinx fly away. He galloped off like a jackal.

"I am seeking for my priests—my priests in their linen robes, with great harps, carrying along a mystic skiff ornamented with pateræ of silver. No more feasts on the lakes! no more illuminations in my Delta! no more cups of milk at Philæ! For a long time Apis has not reappeared.

"Egypt! Egypt! Thy great immovable gods have their shoulders whitened by the dung of birds, and the wind, as it passes along the desert, carries with it the ashes of the dead!—Anubis, protector of shadows, do not leave me!"

The Cynocephalus vanishes.

She gives her child a shaking.

"But what aileth thee? . . . thy hands are cold, thy head fallen back!"

Harpocrates has just died. Then she utters a cry so bitter, mournful, and heartrending, that Antony replies to it by another cry, while he opens his arms to support her.

She is no longer there. He hangs his head, overwhelmed with shame.

All that he has just seen becomes confused in his mind. It is like the stunning effect of a voyage, the uncomfortable sensation of drunkenness. Fain would he hate; and yet a vague pity softens his heart. He begins to weep abundantly.

Hilarion — "What is it now that makes you sad?"

Antony, after questioning himself for a long time — "I am thinking of all the souls lost through these false gods!"

Hilarion — "Do you not find that they have — in some respects — resemblances to the true?"

Antony — "This is a trick of the Devil the better to seduce the faithful. He attacks the strong through the spirit, and the others through the flesh."

Hilarion — "But lust, in its furies, possesses the disinterestedness of penitence. The frantic love of the body accelerates its destruction — and by its weakness proclaims the extent of the impossible."

Antony — "How is it that this affects me? My heart revolts with disgust against those brutish gods, always occupied with carnage and incest."

Hilarion — "Recall to yourself in the Scriptures all the things that scandalise you because you cannot understand them. In the same way, these gods, under the outward form of criminals, may contain the truth. There are some of them left to see. Turn aside!"

7—9

Antony — "No! no! it is a peril!"

Hilarion — "A moment ago you wished to make their acquaintance. Do falsehoods make your faith totter? What do you fear?"

The rocks in front of Antony have become a mountain.

A range of clouds intersects it half-way from the top; and overhead appears another mountain, enormous, quite green, which hollows out the valley unevenly, having on its summit, in a wood of laurels, a palace of bronze, with tiles of gold and ivory capitals.

In the midst of the peristyle, upon a throne, Jupiter, colossal, and with a naked torso, holds victory in one hand, and the thunderbolt in the other; and his eagle, between his legs, erects its head.

Juno, close to him, rolls her great eyes, surmounted by a diadem, from which escapes, like a vapour, a veil floating in the wind.

Behind, Minerva, standing on a pedestal, leans upon her spear. The Gorgon's skin covers her breast, and a linen peplum descends in regular folds even to her toe-nails. Her grey eyes, which shine beneath her vizor, gaze intently into the distance.

At the right of the palace the aged Neptune is riding on a dolphin beating with its fins a vast expanse of azure, which is the sky or the sea, for the perspective of the ocean prolongs the blue ether; the two elements become mingled in one.

On the other side, Pluto, fierce, in a mantle black as night, with a tiara of diamonds and a sceptre of ebony, is in the midst of an isle enclosed by the windings of the Styx; — and this ghostly stream rushes into the darkness, which forms under the cliff a great black gap, a shapeless abyss.

Mars, clad in bronze, brandishes, with an air of fury, his huge sword and shield.

Hercules, standing lower, gazes up at him, leaning on his club.

Apollo, with radiant face, is driving, with his right arm extended, four white horses at a gallop; and Ceres, in a chariot drawn by oxen, is advancing towards him with a sickle in her hand.

Bacchus goes before her on a very low car slowly drawn along by lynxes. Erect, beardless, with vine-branches over his forehead, he passes, holding a goblet from which wine is flowing. Silenus, at his side, is dangling upon an ass. Pan, with pointed ears, is blowing his pipe; the Mimallones beat drums; Mænads scatter flowers; the Bacchantes throw back their heads with hair dishevelled.

Diana, with her tunic tucked up, sets out from the wood with her nymphs.

At the bottom of a cavern, Vulcan is hammering the iron between the Cabiri; here and there, the old river-gods, resting upon green stones, water their urns; and the Muses, standing up, are singing in the dales.

The Hours, of equal height, hold each other by the hand; and Mercury is placed in a slanting posture, upon a rainbow, with his magic wand, his winged sandals and his broad-brimmed hat.

But at the top of the staircase of the gods, amid clouds soft as feathers, whose folds as they wind around let fall roses, Venus Anadyomene is gazing at her image in a mirror; her pupils cast languishing glances underneath her rather heavy eyelashes. She has long, fair tresses, which spread out over her shoulders, her dainty breasts, her slender figure, her hips widening like the curves of a lyre, her two rounded thighs, the dimples around her knees, and her delicate feet. Not far from her mouth a butterfly is fluttering. The splendour of her body sheds around her a halo of brilliant mother-of-pearl; and all the rest of Olympus is bathed in a rosy dawn, which, by insensible degrees, reaches the heights of the azure sky.

Antony — "Ah! my bosom dilates. A joy, which I cannot analyse, descends into the depths of my soul. How beautiful it is! how beautiful it is!"

Hilarion — "They stooped down from the height of the clouds to direct the swords. You might meet them on the roadsides. You kept them in your home; and this familiarity made life divine.

"Her only aim was to be free and beautiful. Her ample robes rendered her movements more graceful. The orator's voice, exercised beside the sea, struck the marble porticoes in unison with the sonorous waves. The stripling, rubbed with oil, wrestled, quite naked, in the full light of day. The most religious action was to expose pure forms.

"Those men, too, respected spouses, the aged and suppliants. Behind the Temple of Hercules, an altar was raised to Pity.

"They used to immolate victims with flowers around their fingers. Memory was not even troubled by the decay of the dead, for there remained of them only a handful of ashes. The soul, mingled with the boundless ether, ascended to the gods!"

Bending towards Antony's ear:

"And they live for ever! The Emperor Constantine adores Apollo. You will find the Trinity in the mysteries of Samothrace, baptism in the case of Isis, the redemption in that of Mithra, the martyrdom of a god in the feasts of Bacchus. Proserpine is the Virgin; Aristæus, Jesus!"

Antony keeps his eyes cast down; then all at once he repeats the creed of Jerusalem—as he recollects it —emitting, after each phrase, a long sigh:

"'I believe in one only God, the Father;—and in one only Lord, Jesus Christ, first-born son of God, who became incarnate and was made man; who was crucified and buried; who ascended into Heaven; who will come to judge the living and the dead; whose kingdom will have no end;—and in one only Holy Ghost;—and in one only baptism of repentance; —and in one holy Catholic Church;—and in the resurrection of the flesh;—and in the life everlasting!'"

Immediately the cross becomes larger, and, piercing the clouds, it casts a shadow over the heaven of the gods.

They all grow dim. Olympus vanishes.

Antony distinguishes near its base, half lost in the caverns, or supporting the stones on their shoulders, huge bodies chained. These are the Titans, the Giants, the Hecatonchires, and the Cyclops.

A voice rises, indistinct and formidable,—like the murmur of the waves, like the sound heard in woods during a storm, like the roaring of the wind down a precipice:

"We knew it, we of all others! The gods were doomed to die. Uranus was mutilated by Saturn, and Saturn by Jupiter. He will be himself annihilated. Each in its turn. It is destiny!"

And, by degrees, they plunge into the mountain, and disappear.

Meanwhile, the roof of the palace of gold flies away.

Jupiter descends from his throne. The thunder at his feet smokes like a brand that is almost extinguished; and the eagle, stretching its neck, gathers with its beak its falling plumes.

"So, then, I am no longer the master of things, all-good, all-powerful, god of the phratriæ and of the Greek peoples, ancestor of all the kings, the Agamemnon of Heaven!

"Eagle of the apotheoses, what breath of Erebus has driven thee to me? or, flying from the Campus Martius, dost thou bring to me the soul of the last of the Emperors?

"I no longer desire those of men! Let the earth guard them, and let them be moved on a level with its baseness. They now have hearts of slaves; they forget injuries, ancestors, oaths; and everywhere the folly of mobs, the mediocrity of the individual, and the hideousness of races reign supreme!"

His respiration makes his sides swell even to bursting, and he writhes with his hands. Hebe in tears presents a cup to him. He seizes it:

"No! no! As long as there will be, no matter where, a head enclosing thought which hates disorder and realises the idea of Law, the spirit of Jupiter will live!"

But the cup is empty. He turns it around slowly on his finger-nail.

"Not a drop! When ambrosia fails, there is an end of the Immortals!"

It slips out of his hand, and he leans against a pillar, feeling that he is dying.

Juno—"There was no need of so many loves! Eagle, bull, swan, golden shower, cloud and flame, thou hast assumed every form, scattered thy light in

into shells, all are dead! The gaiety of the sea has vanished!

"I will not survive it! Let the vast ocean cover me."

He disappears into the azure.

Diana, attired in black, among her dogs, who have become wolves —

"The freedom of great woods intoxicated me with its odour of deer and exhalations of swamps. The women, over whose pregnancy I watched, bring dead children into the world. The moon trembles under the incantations of sorcerers. I am filled with violent and boundless desires. I long to drink poisons, to lose myself in vapours or in dreams! . . ."

And a passing cloud bears her away.

Mars, bare-headed and blood-stained —

"At first, I fought single-handed, provoking by insults an entire army, indifferent to countries, and for the pleasure of carnage. Then, I had companions. They marched to the sound of flutes, in good order, with even step, breathing upon their bucklers, with lofty plume and slanting spear. We flung ourselves into the battle with loud cries like those of eagles. War was as joyous as a feast. Three hundred men withstood all Asia.

"But they returned, those barbarians! and in tens of thousands, nay, in millions! Since numbers, war-engines, and strategy are more powerful, it is better to make an end of it, like a brave man!"

He kills himself.

Vulcan, wiping the sweat from his limbs with a sponge—

"The world is getting cold. It is necessary to heat the springs, the volcanoes, and the rivers, which run from metals under the earth! — Strike harder! with vigorous arm! with all your strength!"

The Cabiri hurt themselves with their hammers, blind themselves with the sparks, and, groping their way along, are lost in the shadow.

Ceres, standing in her chariot which is drawn by wheels having wings in their naves — "Stop! Stop!

"They had good reason to exclude the strangers, the atheists, the epicureans, and the Christians! The mystery of the basket is unveiled, the sanctuary profaned — all is lost!"

She descends with a rapid fall — bursting into exclamation of despair, and dragging back the horses.

"Ah! falsehood! Daira is not given up to me. The brazen bell calls me to the dead. It is another kind of Tartarus. There is no returning from it. Horror!"

The abyss swallows her up.

Bacchus, laughing frantically:

"What does it matter! The wife of Archontes is my spouse! Even the law goes down before drunkenness. For me the new song and the multiplied forms!

"The fire which consumed my mother runs in my veins. Let it burn the stronger, even though I perish!

"Male and female, good for both, I deliver myself to ye, Bacchantes! I deliver myself to ye, Bacchantes! and the vine will twist around the trunks of trees! Howl! dance! writhe! Unbind the tiger and the slave! bite the flesh with ferocious teeth!"

And Pan, Silenus, the Satyrs, the Bacchantes, the Mimallones, and the Mænades, with their serpents, their torches, and their black masks, scatter flowers, then shake their dulcimers, strike their thyrsi, pelt each other with shells, crunch grapes, strangle a he-goat, and rend Bacchus.

Apollo, lashing his coursers, whose glistening hairs fly off —

"I have left behind me Delos the stony, so empty that everything there now seems dead; and I am striving to reach the Delphian oracle before its inspiring vapour should be completely lost. The mules browse on its laurel. The pythoness, gone astray, is found there no longer.

"By a stronger concentration, I will have sublime poems, eternal monuments; and all matter will be penetrated with the vibrations of my cithara."

He fingers its chords. They break and snap against his face. He flings down the instrument, and driving his four-horse chariot furiously:

"No! enough of forms! Farther still — to the very summit — to the world of pure thought!"

But the horses, falling back, begin to prance so that the chariot is smashed; and, entangled in the fragments of the pole and the knottings of the horses, he falls head-foremost into the abyss.

The sky is darkened. Venus, blue as a violet from the cold, shivers.

"I covered with my girdle the entire horizon of Hellas. Its fields shone with the roses of my cheeks; its shores were cut according to the form of my lips; and its mountains, whiter than my doves, palpitated under the hands of the sculptors. My spirit showed itself in the order of festivities, the arrangements of head-dresses, the dialogues of philosophers, and the constitution of republics. But I have loved men too much. It is Love that has dishonoured me!"

She falls back in tears.

"The world is abominable. My bosom feels the lack of air.

"O Mercury, inventor of the lyre, and conductor of souls, bear me away!"

She places a finger upon her mouth, and, describing an immense parabola, topples over into the abyss.

And now nothing can be seen. The darkness is complete.

In the meantime two red arrows seem to escape from the pupils of Hilarion.

Antony at length notices his high stature:

"Many times already, while you were speaking, you appeared to me to be growing tall; and it was not an illusion. How is this? Explain it to me. Your appearance appals me!"

Steps draw nigh.

"What is this now?"

Hilarion stretches forth his arms:

"Look!"

Then, under a pale ray of the moon, Antony distinguishes an interminable caravan which defiles over the crest of the rocks; and each passenger, one after another, falls from the cliff into the gulf.

First, there are the three great gods of Samothrace — Axieros, Axiokeros, and Axiokersa — joined in a cluster, with purple masks, and their hands raised.

Æsculapius advances with a melancholy air, without even seeing Samos and Telesphorus, who question him with anguish. Sosipolis, the Elean, with the form of a python, rolls out his rings towards the abyss. Doespœna, through vertigo, flings herself in there of her own accord. Britomartis, shrieking with fear, clasps the folds of her fillet. The Centaurs arrive with a great galloping, and dash, pell-mell, into the black hole.

Limping behind them come the sad group of nymphs. Those of the meadows are covered with dust; those of the woods groan and bleed, wounded by the woodcutters' axes.

The Gelludæ, the Stryges, the Empusæ, all the infernal goddesses intermingling their hooks, their torches, and their snakes, form a pyramid; and at the summit, upon a vulture's skin, Eurynomus, bluish like flesh-flies, devours his own arms.

Then in a whirlwind disappears at the same time, Orthia the sanguinary, Hymnia of Orchomena, the Saphria of the Patræans, Aphia of Ægina, Bendis of Thrace, and Stymphalia with the leg of a bird. Triopas, in place of three eyeballs, has nothing more than three orbits. Erichthonius, with spindle-shanks, crawls like a cripple on his wrists.

Hilarion—"What happiness, is it not, to see all of them in a state of abjectness and agony? Mount with me on this stone, and you will be like Xerxes reviewing his army.

"Yonder, at a great distance, in the midst of fogs, do you perceive that giant with yellow beard who lets fall a sword red with blood? He is the Scythian Zalmoxis between two planets — Artimpasa, Venus; and Orsiloche, the Moon.

"Farther off, emerging out of the pale clouds, are the gods who are adored by the Cimmerians, beyond even Thule!

"Their great halls were warm, and by the light of the naked swords that covered the vault they drank hydromel in horns of ivory. They ate the liver of the whale in copper plates forged by the demons, or else they listened to the captive sorcerers sweeping their hands across the harps of stone. They are weary! they are cold! The snow wears down their bearskins, and their feet are exposed through the rents in their sandals.

"They mourn for the meadows where, upon hillocks of grass, they used to recover breath in the battle, the long ships whose prows cut through the mountains of ice, and the skates they used in order to follow the orbit of the poles while carrying on the extremities of their arms the firmament, which turned around with them."

A shower of hoar-frost pours down upon them. Antony lowers his glance to the opposite side, and he perceives — outlining themselves in black upon a red background — strange personages with chin-pieces and gauntlets, who throw balls at one another, leap one on top of the other, make grimaces, and dance frantically.

Hilarion — "These are the gods of Etruria, the innumerable Æsars. Here is Tages, the inventor of auguries. He attempts with one hand to increase the divisions of the heavens, while with the other he leans upon the earth. Let him come back to it!

"Nortia is contemplating the wall into which she drove nails to mark the number of the years. Its surface is covered and its last period accomplished. Like two travellers driven about by a tempest, Kastur and Polutuk take shelter under the same mantle."

Antony, closes his eyes — "Enough! Enough!"

But now through the air with a great noise of wings pass all the Victories of the Capitol, hiding their foreheads in their hands, and losing the trophies suspended from their arms.

Janus, master of the twilight, flies away upon a black ram, and of his two faces one is already putrefied, while the other is benumbed with fatigue.

Summanus—god of the gloomy sky, who no longer has a head—presses against his heart an old cake in the form of a wheel.

Vesta, under a ruined cupola, tries to rekindle her extinguished lamp.

Bellona gashes her cheeks without causing the blood, which used to purify her devotees, to flow out.

Antony—"Pardon! They weary me!"

Hilarion—"Formerly they used to be entertaining!"

And he points out to Antony, in a grove of beech-trees a woman perfectly naked—with four paws like a beast—bestridden by a black man holding in each hand a torch.

"This is the goddess Aricia with the demon Virbius. Her priest, the monarch of the woods, happened to be an assassin; and the fugitive slaves, the despoilers of corpses, the brigands of the Salarian road, the cripples of the Sublician bridge, all the vermin of the garrets of the Suburra, had not dearer devotion!

"The patrician ladies of Mark Antony's time preferred Libitina."

And he shows him under the cypresses and rose-trees another woman clothed in gauze. She smiles, though she is surrounded by pickaxes, litters, black hangings, and all the utensils of funerals. Her diamonds glitter from afar among cobwebs. The Larvæ, like skeletons, display their bones amid the branches, and the Lemures, who are phantoms, spread out their bats' wings.

On the side of a field the god Terma is bent down, torn asunder, and covered with filth.

In the midst of a ridge the huge corpse of Vertumnus is being devoured by red dogs. The rustic gods depart weeping, Sartor, Sarrator, Vervactor, Eollina, Vallona, and Hostilenus — all covered with little hooded cloaks, and each bearing a mattock, a fork, a hurdle, and a boar-spear.

Hilarion — "It was their spirits that made the villa prosper with its dove-cotes, its park for dormice, its poultry-yards protected by snares, and its hot stables embalmed with cedar.

"They protected all the wretched people who dragged the fetters with their legs over the pebbles of the Sabina, those who called the hogs with the sound of the trumpet, those who gathered the grapes on the tops of the elm-trees, those who drove through the by-roads the asses laden with dung. The husbandman, while he panted over the handle of his plough, prayed to them to strengthen his arms; and the cow-herds, in the shadow of the lime-trees, beside gourds of milk, chanted their eulogies by turns upon flutes of reeds."

Antony sighs.

And in the middle of a chamber, upon a platform, a bed of ivory is revealed, surrounded by persons lifting up pine-torches.

"Those are the gods of marriage. They are awaiting the bride.

"Domiduca has to lead her in, Virgo to undo her girdle, Subigo to stretch her upon the bed, and Præma to keep back her arms, whispering sweet words in her ear.

"But she will not come! and they dismiss the others — Nona and Decima, the nurses; the three

Nixii, who are to deliver her; the two wet-nurses, Educa and Potina; and Carna, the cradle-rocker, whose bunch of hawthorns drives away bad dreams from the infant.   Later, Ossipago will have strengthened its knees, Barbatus will have given the beard, Stimula the first desires, and Volupia the first enjoyment; Fabulinus will have taught it how to speak, Numera how to count, Camœna how to sing, and Consus how to think."

The chamber is empty, and there remains no longer at the side of the bed anyone but Nænia — a hundred years old — muttering to herself the lament which she poured forth on the death of old men.

But soon her voice is lost amid bitter cries, which come from the domestic lares, squatted at the end of the atrium, clad in dogs' skins, with flowers around their bodies, holding their closed hands up to their cheeks, and weeping as much as they can.

"Where is the portion of food which is given to us at each meal, the good attentions of maid-servant, the smile of the matron, and the gaiety of the little boys playing with huckle-bones on the mosaic of the courtyard ? Then, when they have grown big, they hang over our breasts their gold or leather bullæ.

"What happiness, when, on the evening of a triumph, the master, returning home, turned towards us his humid eyes! He told the story of his contests, and the narrow house was more stately than a palace, and more sacred than a temple.

"How pleasant were the repasts of the family, especially the day after the Feralia! The feeling of tenderness towards the dead dispelled all discords; and people embraced one another, drinking to the glories of the past, and to the hopes of the future.

"But the ancestors in painted wax, shut up behind us, became gradually covered with mouldiness. The new races, to punish us for their own deceptions, have broken our jaws; and under the rats' teeth our bodies of wood have crumbled away."

And the innumerable gods, watching at the doors, in the kitchen, in the cellar, and in the stoves, disperse on all sides, under the appearance of enormous ants running away, or huge butterflies on the wing.

Then a thunderclap.

A voice—"I was the God of armies, the Lord, the Lord God!

"I have unfolded on the hills the tents of Jacob, and nourished in the sands my fugitive people. It was I who burned Sodom! It was I who engulfed the earth beneath the Deluge! It was I who drowned Pharaoh, with the royal princes, the war-chariots, and the charioteers. A jealous God, I execrated the other gods. I crushed the impure; I overthrew the proud; and my desolation rushed to right and left, like a dromedary let loose in a field of maize.

"To set Israel free, I chose the simple. Angels, with wings of flame, spoke to them in the bushes.

"Perfumed with spikenard, cinnamon, and myrrh, with transparent robes and high-heeled shoes, women of intrepid heart went forth to slay the captains. The passing wind bore away the prophets.

"I engraved my law on tablets of stone. It shut in my people as in a citadel. They were my people. I was their God! The earth was mine, and men were mine, with their thoughts, their works, the implements with which they tilled the soil, and their posterity.

"My ark rested in a triple sanctuary, behind purple curtains and flaming lamps. For my ministry I

had an entire tribe, who swung the censers, and the
high-priest in a robe of hyacinth, and wearing
precious stones upon his breast arranged in regular
order.

"Woe! woe! The Holy of Holies is flung open;
the veil is rent; the odours of the holocaust are scattered to all the winds. The jackals whine in the
sepulchres; my temple is destroyed; my people are
dispersed!

"They have strangled the priests with the cords
of their vestments. The women are captives; the
sacred vessels are all melted down!"

The voice, dying away:

"I was the God of armies, the Lord, the Lord
God!" Then comes an appalling silence, a profound
darkness.

Antony — "They are all gone!"

"I remain!" says some one.

And, face to face with him stands Hilarion, but
transfigured — beautiful as an archangel, luminous as
a sun, and so tall that, in order to see him, Antony
lifts up his head — "Who, then, are you?"

Hilarion — "My kingdom is as wide as the universe, and my desire has no limits. I am always going about enfranchising the mind and weighing the
worlds, without hate, without fear, without love, and
without God. I am called Science."

Antony, recoiling backwards — "You must be,
rather, the Devil!"

Hilarion, fixing his eyes upon him — "Do you
wish to see him?"

Antony no longer avoids his glance. He is seized
with curiosity concerning the Devil. His terror increases; his longing becomes measureless.

"If I saw him, however — if I saw him?" . . .
Then, in a spasm of rage:

"The horror that I have of him will rid me of
him forever. Yes!"

A cloven foot reveals itself. Antony is filled with
regret. But the Devil overshadows him with his
horns, and carries him off.

CHAPTER VI.

The Mystery of Space.

HE FLIES under Antony's body, extended like a swimmer; his two great wings, outspread, entirely concealing him, resemble a cloud.

Antony —"Where am I going? Just now I caught a glimpse of the form of the Accursèd One. No! a cloud is carrying me away. Perhaps I am dead, and am mounting up to God? . . .

"Ah! how well I breathe! The untainted air inflates my soul. No more heaviness! no more suffering!

"Beneath me, the thunderbolt darts forth, the horizon widens, rivers cross one another. That light spot is the desert; that pool of water the ocean. And other oceans appear — immense regions of which I had no knowledge. There are black lands that smoke like live embers, a belt of snow ever obscured by the mists. I am trying to discover the mountains where each evening the sun goes to sleep."

The Devil — "The sun never goes to sleep!"

Antony is not startled by this voice. It appears to him an echo of his thought — a response of his memory.

Meanwhile, the earth takes the form of a ball, and he perceives it in the midst of the azure turning on its poles while it winds around the sun.

The Devil — "So, then, it is not the centre of the world? Pride of man, humble thyself!"

Antony — "I can scarcely distinguish it now. It is intermingled with the other fires. The firmament is but a tissue of stars."

They continue to ascend.

"No noise! not even the crying of the eagles! Nothing! . . . and I bend down to listen to the music of the spheres."

The Devil — "You cannot hear them! No longer will you see the antichthon of Plato, the focus of Philolaüs, the spheres of Aristotle, or the seven heavens of the Jews with the great waters above the vault of crystal!"

Antony — "From below it appeared as solid as a wall. But now, on the contrary, I am penetrating it; I am plunging into it!"

And he arrives in front of the moon — which is like a piece of ice, quite round, filled with a motionless light.

The Devil — "This was formerly the abode of souls. The good Pythagoras had even supplied it with birds and magnificent flowers."

Antony — "I see nothing there save desolate plains, with extinct craters, under a black sky.

"Come towards those stars with a softer radiance, so that we may gaze upon the angels who hold them with the ends of their arms, like torches!"

The Devil carries him into the midst of the stars.

"They attract one another at the same time that they repel one another. The action of each has an

effect on the others, and helps to produce their movements — and all this without the medium of an aux-
iliary, by the force of a law, by the virtue simply of
order."

Antony — "Yes . . . yes! my intelligence
grasps it! It is a joy greater than the sweetness of
affection! I pant with stupefaction before the immensity of God!"

The Devil — "Like the firmament, which rises in
proportion as you ascend, He will become greater
according as your imagination mounts higher; and
you will feel your joy increase in proportion to the
unfolding of the universe, in this enlargement of the
Infinite."

Antony — "Ah! higher! ever higher!"

The stars multiply and shed around their scintilla-
tions. The Milky Way at the zenith spreads out like
an immense belt, with gaps here and there; in these
clefts, amid its brightness, dark tracts reveal themselves. There are showers of stars, trains of golden
dust, luminous vapours which float and then dissolve.

Sometimes a comet sweeps by suddenly; then the
tranquillity of the countless lights is renewed.

Antony, with open arms, leans on the Devil's two
horns, thus occupying the entire space covered by
his wings. He recalls with disdain the ignorance of
former days, the limitation of his ideas. Here, then,
close beside him, were those luminous globes which
he used to gaze at from below. He traces the crossing of their paths, the complexity of their directions. He sees them coming from afar, and, suspended like stones in a sling, describing their orbits
and pushing forward their parabolas.

He perceives, with a single glance, the Southern Cross and the Great Bear, the Lynx and the Centaur, the nebulæ of the Gold-fish, the six suns in the constellation of Orion, Jupiter with his four satellites, and the triple ring of the monstrous Saturn! all the planets, all the stars which men should, in future days, discover! He fills his eyes with their light; he overloads his mind with a calculation of their distances; — then he lets his head fall once more.

"What is the object of all this?"

The Devil — "There is no object!

"How could God have had an object? What experience could have enlightened Him, what reflection enabled Him to judge? Before the beginning of things, it would not have operated, and now it would be useless."

Antony — "Nevertheless, He created the world, at one period of time, by His mere word!"

The Devil — "But the beings who inhabit the earth came there successively. In the same way, in the sky, new stars arise — different effects from various causes."

Antony — "The variety of causes is the will of God!"

The Devil — "But to admit in God several acts of will is to admit several causes, and thus to destroy His unity!

"His will is not separable from His essence. He cannot have a second will, inasmuch as He cannot have a second essence — and, since He exists eternally, He acts eternally.

"Look at the sun! From its borders escape great flames emitting sparks which scatter themselves to become new worlds; and, further than the last, beyond those depths where only night is visible, other suns whirl round, and behind these others again, and others still, to infinity . . ."

Antony—"Enough! enough! I am terrified! I am about to fall into the abyss."

The Devil stops, and gently balancing himself—

"There is no such thing as nothingness! There is no vacuum! Everywhere there are bodies moving over the unchangeable realms of space—and, as if it had any bounds it would not be space but a body, it consequently has no limits!"

Antony, open-mouthed—"No limits!"

The Devil—"Ascend into the sky forever and ever, and you will never reach the top! Descend beneath the earth for millions upon millions of centuries, and you will never get to the bottom—inasmuch as there is no bottom, no top, no end, above or below; and space is, in fact, comprised in God, who is not a part of space, of a magnitude that can be measured, but immensity!"

Antony, slowly—"Matter, in that case, would be part of God?"

The Devil—"Why not? Can you tell where He comes to an end?"

Antony—"On the contrary, I prostrate myself, I efface myself before His power!"

The Devil—"And you pretend to move Him! You speak to Him, you even adorn Him with virtues—goodness, justice, clemency,—in place of recognising the fact that He possesses all perfections!

"To conceive anything beyond is to conceive God outside of God. Being outside of Being. But then He is the only Being, the only Substance.

"If substance could be divided, it would lose its nature—it would not be itself; God would no longer exist. He is, therefore, indivisible as well as infinite, and if He had a body, He would be made up of parts. He would no longer be one; He would no longer be infinite. Therefore, He is not a person!"

Antony — "What? My prayers, my sobs, the sufferings of my flesh, the transports of my zeal, all these things would be no better than a lie . . . in space . . . uselessly — like a bird's cry, like a whirlwind of dead leaves!"

He weeps.

"Oh! no! There is above everything some One, a Great Spirit, a Lord, a Father, whom my heart adores, and who must love me!"

The Devil — "You desire that God should not be God; for, if He experienced love, anger, or pity, He would pass from His perfection to a greater or less perfection. He cannot descend to a sentiment, or be contained under a form."

Antony — "One day, however, I shall see Him!"

The Devil — "With the Blessèd, is it not? When the finite shall enjoy the Infinite, enclosing the Absolute in a limited space!"

Antony — "No matter! There must be a Paradise for the good, as well as a Hell for the wicked!"

The Devil — "Does the exigency of your reason constitute the law of things? Without doubt, evil is a matter of indifference to God, seeing that the earth is covered with it!

"Is it from impotence that He endures it, or from cruelty that He preserves it?

"Do you think that He can be continually putting the world in order like an imperfect work, and that He watches over all the movements of all beings, from the flight of the butterfly to the thought of man?

"If He created the universe His providence is superfluous. If Providence exists, creation is defective.

"But good and evil only concern you — like day and night, pleasure and pain, death and birth, which have relationship merely to a corner of space, to a special medium, to a particular interest. Inasmuch as what is infinite alone is permanent, the Infinite exists; and that is all!"

The Devil has gradually extended his huge wings, and now they cover space.

Antony can no longer see. He is on the point of fainting:

"A horrible chill freezes me to the bottom of my soul. This exceeds the utmost pitch of pain. It is, as it were, a death more profound than death. I wheel through the immensity of darkness. It enters into me. My consciousness is shivered to atoms under this expansion of nothingness."

The Devil — "But things happen only through the medium of your mind. Like a concave mirror, it distorts objects, and you need every resource in order to verify facts.

"Never shall you understand the universe in its full extent; consequently you cannot form an idea as to its cause, so as to have a just notion of God, or even say that the universe is infinite, for you should first comprehend the Infinite!

"Form is perhaps an error of your senses, substance an illusion of your intellect. Unless it be that the world, being a perpetual flux of things, appearances, by a sort of contradiction, would not be a test of truth, and illusion would be the only reality.

"But are you sure that you see? Are you sure that you live? Perhaps nothing at all exists!"

The Devil has seized Antony, and, holding him by the extremities of his arms, stares at him with open jaws ready to swallow him up.

"Come, adore me! and curse the phantom that you call God!"

Antony raises his eyes with a last movement of lingering hope.

The Devil quits him.

CHAPTER VII.

THE CHIMERA AND THE SPHINX.

ANTONY finds himself stretched on his back at the edge of the cliff.

The sky is beginning to grow white.

"Is this the brightness of dawn? or is it the reflection of the moon?"

He tries to rise, then sinks back, and with chattering teeth:

"I feel fatigued . . . as if all my bones were broken!

"Why?

"Ah! it is the Devil! I remember; and he even repeated to me all I had learned from old Didymus concerning the opinions of Xenophanes, of Heraclitus, of Melissus, and of Anaxagoras, as well as concerning the Infinite, the creation, and the impossibility of knowing anything!

"And I imagined that I could unite myself to God!"

Laughing bitterly:

"Ah! madness! madness! Is it my fault? Prayer is intolerable to me! My heart is drier than a rock! Formerly it overflowed with love! . . .

"The sand, in the morning, used to send forth exhalations on the horizon, like the fumes of a censer. At the setting of the sun blossoms of fire burst forth from the cross, and, in the middle of the night, it often seemed to me that all creatures and all things, gathered in the same silence, were with me adoring the Lord. Oh! charm of prayer, bliss of ecstasy, gifts of Heaven, what has become of you?

"I remember a journey I made with Ammon in search of a solitude in which we might establish monasteries. It was the last evening, and we quickened our steps, murmuring hymns, side by side, without uttering a word. In proportion as the sun went down, the shadows of our bodies lengthened, like two obelisks, always enlarging and marching on in front of us. With the pieces of our staffs we planted the cross here and there to mark the site of a cell. The night came on slowly, and black waves spread over the earth, while an immense sheet of red still occupied the sky.

"When I was a child, I used to amuse myself in constructing hermitages with pebbles. My mother, close beside me, used to watch what I was doing.

"She was going to curse me for abandoning her, tearing her white locks. And her corpse remained stretched in the middle of the cell, beneath the roof of reeds, between the tottering walls. Through a hole, a hyena, sniffing, thrusts forward his jaws!
. . . Horror! horror!"

He sobs.

"No: Ammonaria would not have left her!

"Where is Ammonaria now?

"Perhaps, in a hot bath she is drawing off her garments one by one, first her cloak, then her girdle, then her outer tunic, then her inner one, then the wrappings round her neck; and the vapour of cinnamon envelops her naked limbs. At last she sinks to sleep on the tepid floor. Her hair, falling around her hips, looks like a black fleece — and, almost suffocating in the overheated atmosphere, she draws breath, with her body bent forward and her breasts projecting. Hold! here is my flesh breaking into revolt. In the midst of anguish, I am tortured by voluptuousness. Two punishments at the same time — it is too much! I can no longer endure my own body!"

He stoops down and gazes over the precipice.

"The man who falls over that will be killed. Nothing easier, by simply rolling over on the left side: it is necessary to take only one step! only one!"

Then appears an old woman.

Antony rises with a start of error. He imagines that he sees his mother risen from the dead.

But this one is much older and excessively emaciated. A winding-sheet, fastened round her head, hangs with her white hair down to the very extremities of her legs, thin as sticks. The brilliancy of her teeth, which are like ivory, makes her clayey skin look darker. The sockets of her eyes are full of gloom, and in their depths flicker two flames, like lamps in a sepulchre.

"Come forward," she says; "what keeps you back?"

Antony, stammering — "I am afraid of committing a sin!"

She resumes:

"But King Saul was slain! Razias, a just man, was slain! Saint Pelagius of Antioch was slain!

Dominius of Aleppo and his two daughters, three more saints, were slain; — and recall to your mind all the confessors who, in their eagerness to die, rushed to meet their executioners. In order to taste death the more speedily, the virgins of Miletus strangled themselves with their cords. The philosopher, Hegesias, at Syracuse preached so well on the subject, that people deserted the brothels to hang themselves in the fields. The Roman patricians sought for death as if it were a debauch."

Antony — "Yes, it is a powerful passion! Many an anchorite has yielded to it."

The old woman — "To do a thing which makes you equal to God — think of that! He created you; you are about to destroy His work, you, by your courage, freely. The enjoyment of Erostrates was not greater. And then, your body is thus mocked by your soul in order that you may avenge yourself in the end. You will have no pain. It will soon be over. What are you afraid of? A large black hole! It is empty, perhaps!"

Antony listens without saying anything in reply; — and, on the other side, appears another woman, marvellously young and beautiful. At first, he takes her for Ammonaria. But she is taller, fair as honey, rather plump, with paint on her cheeks, and roses on her head. Her long robe, covered with spangles, is studded with metallic mirrors. Her fleshly lips have a look of blood, and her somewhat heavy eyelashes are so much bathed in languor that one would imagine she was blind. She murmurs:

"Come, then, and enjoy yourself. Solomon recommends pleasure. Go where your heart leads you, and according to the desire of your eyes."

Antony — "To find what pleasure? My heart is sick; my eyes are dim!"

She replies:

"Hasten to the suburb of Racotis; push open a door painted blue; and, when you are in the atrium, where a jet of water is gurgling, a woman will present herself — in a peplum of white silk edged with gold, her hair dishevelled, and her laugh like sounds made by rattlesnakes. She is clever. In her caress you will taste the pride of an initiation, and the satisfaction of a want. Have you pressed against your bosom a maiden who loved you? Recall to your mind her remorse, which vanished under a flood of sweet tears. You can imagine yourself — can you not? — walking through the woods beneath the light of the moon. At the pressure of your hands joined with hers a shudder runs through both of you; your eyes, brought close together, overflow from one to the other like immaterial waves, and your heart is full; it is bursting; it is a delicious whirlwind, an overpowering intoxication."

The old woman — "You need not experience joys to feel their bitterness! You need only see them from afar, and disgust takes possession of you. You must needs be wearied with the monotony of the same actions, the duration of the days, the ugliness of the world, and the stupidity of the sun!"

Antony — "Oh! yes; all that it shines upon is displeasing to me."

The young woman — "Hermit! hermit! you shall find diamonds among the pebbles, fountains beneath the sand, a delight in the dangers which you despise; and there are even places on the earth so beautiful that you are filled with a longing to embrace them."

7—11

The old woman—"Every evening when you lie down to sleep on the earth, you hope that it may soon cover you."

The young woman—"Nevertheless, you believe in the resurrection of the flesh, which is the transport of life into eternity."

The old woman, while speaking, has been growing more emaciated, and, above her skull, which has no hair upon it, a bat has been making circles in the air.

The young woman has become plumper. Her robe changes colour; her nostrils swell; her eyes roll softly.

The first says, opening her arms:

"Come! I am consolation, rest, oblivion, eternal peace!"

And the second offering her breast:

"I am the soother, the joy, the life, the happiness inexhaustible!"

Antony turns on his heel to fly. Each of them places a hand upon his shoulder.

The winding-sheet flies open, and reveals the skeleton of Death. The robe bursts open, and presents to view the entire body of Lust, which has a slender figure, with an enormous development behind, and great, undulating masses of hair, disappearing towards the end.

Antony remains motionless between the pair, contemplating them.

Death says to him—

"This moment, or a little later—what does it matter? You belong to me, like the suns, the nations, the cities, the kings, the snow on the mountains, and the grass in the fields. I fly higher than the sparrow-hawk, I run more quickly than the gazelle; I keep pace even with hope; I have conquered God!"

Lust— "Do not resist; I am omnipotent. The forests echo with my sighs; the waves are stirred by my agitations. Virtue, courage, piety, are dissolved in the perfume of my breath. I accompany man at every step he takes; and on the threshold of the tomb he comes back to me."

Death — "I will reveal to you what you tried to grasp by the light of torches on the features of the dead — or when you rambled beyond the Pyramids in those vast sand-heaps composed of human remains. From time to time, a piece of skull rolled under your sandal. You took it out of the dust; you made it slip between your fingers; and your mind, becoming absorbed in it, was plunged into nothingness."

Lust—"Mine is a deeper gulf! Marble slabs have inspired impure loves. People rush towards meetings that terrify them, and rivet the very chains which they curse. Whence comes the witchery of courtesans, the extravagance of dreams, the immensity of my sadness?"

Death—"My irony surpasses that of all other things. There are convulsions of joy at the funerals of kings and at the extermination of peoples; and they make war with music, plumes, flags, golden harnesses, and a display of ceremony to pay me the greater homage."

Lust—"My anger is as strong as yours. I howl, I bite, I have sweats of agony, and corpse-like appearances."

Death—"It is I who make you serious; let us embrace each other!"

Death chuckles; Lust roars. They seize each other's figures, and sing together:

"I hasten the dissolution of matter."

"I facilitate the scattering of germs!"

"Thou destroyest that I may renew!"

"Thou engenderest that I may destroy!"

"Active my power!"

"Fruitful my decay!"

And their voices, whose echoes, rolling forth, fill the horizon, become so powerful that Antony falls backward.

A shock, from time to time, causes him to half open his eyes; and he perceives, in the midst of the darkness, a kind of monster before him.

It is a death's-head with a crown of roses. It rises above the torso of a woman white as mother-of-pearl. Beneath, a winding-sheet, starred with points of gold, makes a kind of train;—and the entire body undulates, like a gigantic worm holding itself erect.

The vision grows fainter, and then fades away.

Antony, rises again—"This time, once more, it was the Devil, and under his two-fold aspect—the spirit of voluptuousness and the spirit of destruction. Neither terrifies me. I thrust happiness aside, and feel that I am eternal.

"Thus, death is only an illusion, a veil, masking at certain points the continuity of life. But substance, being one, why is there a variety of forms? There must be somewhere primordial figures, whose bodies are only images. If one could see, one would know the bond between mind and matter, wherein Being consists!

"There are those figures which were painted at Babylon on the wall of the temple of Belus, and they covered a mosaic in the port of Carthage. I, myself, have sometimes seen in the sky what seemed like forms of spirits. Those who traverse the desert meet animals passing all conception . . ."

And, opposite him, on the other side of the Nile, lo! the Sphinx appears.

It stretches out its feet, shakes the fillets on its forehead, and lies down upon its belly.

Jumping, flying, spirting fire through its nostrils, and striking its wings with its dragon's tail, the Chimera with its green eyes, winds round, and barks. The curls of its head, thrown back on one side, intermingle with the hair on its haunches; and on the other side they hang over the sand, and move to and fro with the swaying of its entire body.

The Sphinx is motionless, and gazes at the Chimera:

"Here, Chimera; stop!"

The Chimera—"No, never!"

The Sphinx—"Do not run so quickly; do not fly so high; do not bark so loud!"

The Chimera—"Do not address me, do not address me any more, since you remain forever silent!"

The Sphinx—"Cease casting your flames in my face and flinging your yells in my ears; you shall not melt my granite!"

The Chimera—"You will not get hold of me, terrible Sphinx!"

The Sphinx—"You are too foolish to live with me!"

The Chimera—"You are too clumsy to follow me!"

The Sphinx—"And where are you going that you run so quickly?"

The Chimera—"I gallop into the corridors of the labyrinth; I hover over the mountains; I skim along the waves; I yelp at the bottoms of precipices; I hang by my jaws on the skirts of the clouds. With my trailing tail I scratch the coasts, and the hills have taken their curb according to the form of my shoulders. But as for you, I find you perpetually motionless; or, rather, with the end of your claw tracing letters on the sand."

The Sphinx—"That is because I keep my secret! I reflect and I calculate. The sea returns to its bed; the blades of corn balance themselves in the wind; the caravans pass; the dust flies off; the cities crumble;—but my glance, which nothing can turn aside, remains concentrated on the objects which cover an inaccessible horizon."

The Chimera—"As for me, I am light and joyous! I discover in men dazzling perspectives, with Paradises in the clouds and distant felicities. I pour into their souls the eternal insanities, projects of happiness, plans for the future, dreams of glory, and oaths of love, as well as virtuous resolutions. I drive them on perilous voyages and on mighty enterprises. I have carved with my claws the marvels of architecture. It is I that hung the little bells on the tomb of Porsenna, and surrounded with a wall of Corinthian brass the quays of the Atlantides.

"I seek fresh perfumes, larger flowers, pleasures hitherto unknown. If anywhere I find a man whose soul reposes in wisdom, I fall upon him and strangle him."

The Sphinx—"All those whom the desire of God torments, I have devoured.

"The strongest, in order to climb to my royal

forehead, mount upon the stripes of my fillets as on the steps of a staircase. Weariness takes possession of them, and they fall back of their own accord."

Antony begins to tremble. He is not before his cell, but in the desert, having at either side of him those two monstrous animals, whose jaws graze his shoulders.

The Sphinx—"O Fantasy, bear me on thy wings to enliven thy sadness!"

The Chimera—"O Unknown One, I am in love with thine eyes! I turn round thee, soliciting allayment of that which devours me!"

The Sphinx—"My feet cannot raise themselves. The lichen, like a ringworm, has grown over my mouth. By dint of thinking, I have no longer anything to say."

The Chimera—"You lie, hypocritical Sphinx! How is it that you are always addressing me and abjuring me?"

The Sphinx—"It is you, unmanageable caprice, who pass and whirl about."

The Chimera—"Is that my fault? Come, now, just let me be!"

It barks.

The Sphinx—"You move away; you avoid me!"

The Sphinx grumbles.

The Chimera—"Let us make the attempt! You crush me!"

The Sphinx—"No; impossible!"

And sinking, little by little, it disappears in the sand, while the Chimera, crawling, with its tongue out, departs with a winding movement.

The breath issuing from its mouth has produced a fog.

In this fog Antony traces masses of clouds and imperfect curves. Finally, he distinguishes what appear to be human bodies.

And first advances the group of Astomi, like air-balls passing across the sun.

"Don't puff too strongly! The drops of rain bruise us; the false sounds excoriate us; the darkness blinds us. Composed of breezes and of perfumes, we roll, we float—a little more than dreams, not entirely beings."

The Nisnas have but one eye, one cheek, one hand, one leg, half a body, and half a heart. And they say, in a very loud tone:

"We live quite at our ease in our halves of houses with our halves of wives and our halves of children."

The Blemmyes, absolutely bereft of heads—

"Our shoulders are the largest;—and there is not an ox, a rhinoceros, or an elephant that is capable of carrying what we carry.

"Arrows, and a sort of vague outline are imprinted on our breasts—that is all! We reduce digestion to thought; we subtilise secretions. For us God floats peacefully in the internal chyle.

"We proceed straight on our way, passing through every mire, running along the verge of every abyss; and we are the most industrious, happy, and virtuous people."

The Pygmies—"Little good-fellows, we swarm over the world, like vermin on the hump of a dromedary.

"We are burnt, drowned, or run over; but we always reappear more full of life and more numerous —terrible from the multitude of us that exists!"

The Sciapodes—"Kept on the ground by our

flowing locks, long as creeping plants, we vegetate under the shelter of our feet, which are as large as parasols; and the light reaches us through the spaces between our wide heels. No disorder and no toil! To keep the head as low as possible — that is the secret of happiness!"

Their lifted thighs, resembling trunks of trees, increase in number. And now a forest appears in which huge apes rush along on four paws. They are men with dogs' heads.

The Cynocephali — "We leap from branch to branch to suck the eggs, and we pluck the little birds; then we put their nests upon our heads after the fashion of caps.

"We do not fail to snatch away the worst of the cows, and we destroy the lynxes' eyes. Tearing the flowers, crushing the fruits, agitating the springs, we are the masters — by the strength of our arms and the fierceness of our hearts.

"Be bold, comrades, and snap your jaws!"

Blood and milk flow from their lips. The rain streams over their hairy backs.

Antony inhales the freshness of green leaves which are agitated as the branches of the trees dash against each other. All at once appears a large black stag with a bull's head, carrying between his two ears a mass of white horns.

The Sadhuzag — "My seventy-four antlers are hollow like flutes. When I turn myself towards the south wind, sounds go forth from them that draw around me the ravished beasts. The serpents come winding to my feet; the wasps stick in my nostrils; and the parrots, the doves, and the ibises alight upon my branches. Listen!"

He bends back his horns, from which issues an unutterably sweet music.

Antony presses both his hands above his heart. It seems to him as if this melody were about to carry off his soul.

The Sadhuzag—"But, when I turn towards the north wind, my horns, more bushy than a battalion of spears, emit a howling noise. The forests thrill; the rivers swell; the husks of the fruit burst, and blades of grass stand erect like a coward's hair. Listen!"

He bows down his branches, from which now come forth discordant cries. Antony feels as if he were torn asunder, and his horror is increased on seeing the Mantichor, a gigantic red lion with a human figure and three rows of teeth:

"The silky texture of my scarlet hair mingles with the yellowness of the sands. I breathe through my nostrils the terror of solitudes. I spit forth the plague. I devour armies when they venture into the desert. My nails are twisted like gimlets; my teeth are cut like a saw; and my hair, wriggled out of shape, bristles with darts which I scatter, right and left, behind me. Hold! hold!"

The Mantichor casts thorns from his tail, which radiate, like arrows, in all directions. Drops of blood flow, spattering over the foliage.

The Catoblepas appears, a black buffalo, with a pig's head hanging to the earth, and connected with his shoulders by a slender neck, long and flabby as an empty gut. He is wallowing on the ground; and his feet disappear under the enormous mane of hard hairs that descend over his face:

"Fat, melancholy, savage, I remain continually feeling the mire under my stomach. My skull is so heavy that it is impossible for me to carry it. I roll it around slowly; and, opening my jaws, I snatch with my tongue the poisonous herbs that are moistened with my breath. I once devoured my paws without noticing it.

"No one, Antony, has ever seen my eyes, or those who have seen them are dead. If I but raised my eyelids — my eyelids red and swollen — that instant you would die."

Antony — "Oh! that thing! . . . Well! well! As if I had any such longing! Its stupidity attracts me. No! no! I will not!" He looks fixedly on the ground. But the grass lights up, and, in the twistings of the flames, stands erect the Basilisk, a huge, violet serpent, with a trilobate crest and two teeth — one above, the other below:

"Take care! You are about to fall into my jaws! I drink fire. I am fire myself; and from every quarter I suck it in — from clouds, from pebbles, from dead trees, from the hair of animals, and from the surface of marshes. My temperature supports the volcanoes. I cause the lustre of precious stones and the colour of metals."

The Griffin, a lion with a vulture's beak, white wings, red paws, and blue neck — "I am the master of the profound splendours. I know the secret of the tombs where the old kings sleep. A chain, which issues from the wall, keeps their heads erect. Near them, in basins of porphyry, women whom they have loved float upon black liquids. Their treasures are ranged in halls, in lozenges, in hillocks, and in pyramids; and, lower, far below the tombs, after long journeys in the midst of suffocating darkness, are rivers of gold with forests of diamonds, meadows of carbuncles, and lakes

of quicksilver. With my back against the door of
the vault, and my claws in the air, I watch with
my flaming eyes those who may think fit to come
there. The immense plain, even to the furthest
point of the horizon, is quite bare and whitened
with travellers' bones. For you the bronze doors will
open, and you will inhale the vapour of the mines;
you will descend into the caverns. . . . Quick!
quick!"

He digs the earth with his claws, crowing like a
cock.

A thousand voices reply to him. The forest trembles.

And all sorts of horrible beasts arise: the Tragela-
phus, half-stag, half-ox; the Myrmecoleo, a lion in
front, an ant behind, whose genitals are turned backwards; the python, Aksar, of sixty cubits, who
frightened Moses; the great weasel, Pastinaca, which
kills trees by its odour; the Presteros, which renders
idiotic those who touch it; the Mirag, a horned hare
dwelling in the islands of the sea. The Copard Phal-
mant bursts his belly by dint of howling; the Senad,
a bear with three heads, tears its little ones with its
mouth; the dog, Cepus, scatters on the rocks the blue
milk of its dugs. Mosquitoes begin to buzz, toads to
jump, and serpents to hiss. Lightnings flash; down
comes the hail.

Then there are squalls, which reveal anatomical
marvels. There are alligators' heads with roebucks'
feet, owls with serpents' tails, swine with tigers'
muzzles, goats with asses' rumps, frogs covered with
hair like bears, chameleons large as hippopotami,
calves with two heads, one of which weeps while the
other bellows, four fœtuses holding each other by the

navel and spinning like tops, and winged bellies which flutter like gnats.

They rain down from the sky; they spring out of the ground; they glide from the rocks. Everywhere eyes flash, mouths roar; the breasts bulge out; the claws lengthen; the teeth gnash; the flesh quivers. Some of them bring forth their young; others with a single bite, devour one another.

Suffocating from their very numbers, multiplying by their contact, they climb on top of one another; and they all keep stirring about Antony with a regular swaying motion, as if the soil were the deck of a vessel.

He feels close to his calves the trailing of slugs, and on his hands the cold touch of vipers; and spiders spinning their webs enclose him in their network.

But the circle of monsters begins to open; the sky suddenly becomes blue, and the unicorn makes its appearance:

"Off I gallop! Off I gallop!

"I have hoofs of ivory, teeth of steel, a head coloured purple, a body like snow, and the horn on my forehead has the varied hues of the rainbow.

"I travel from Chaldea to the Tartar desert, on the banks of the Ganges, and into Mesopotamia. I outstrip the ostriches. I run so rapidly that I draw the wind along with me. I rub my back against the palm-trees; I roll myself in the bamboos. With one bound I jump across the rivers. Doves fly above my head. Only a virgin can bridle me.

"Off I gallop! Off I gallop!"

Antony watches him flying away.

And, keeping his eyes still raised, he perceives all the birds that are nourished by the wind: the Gouith, the Ahuti, the Alphalim, the Jukneth from the mountains of Caff, and the Homaï of the Arabs, which are the souls of murdered men. He hears the parrots utter human speech, then the great web-footed Pelasgians, who sob like children or chuckle like old women.

A briny breath of air strikes his nostrils. A sea-shore is now before him.

At a distance rise waterspouts, lashed up by the whales; and at the extremity of the horizon the beasts of the sea, round, like leather bottles, flat, like strips of metal, or indented, like saws, advance, crawling over the sand:

"You are about to come with us into our unfathomable depths, never penetrated by man before. Different races dwell in the country of the ocean. Some are in the abode of the tempests; others swim openly in the transparency of the cold waves, browse like oxen over the coral plains, sniff in with their nostrils the ebbing tide, or carry on their shoulders the weight of the ocean-springs."

Phosphorescences flash from the hairs of the seals and from the scales of the fishes. Sea-hedgehogs turn around like wheels; Ammon's horns unroll themselves like cables; oysters make sounds with the fastenings of their shells; polypi spread out their tentacles; medusæ quiver like crystal balls; sponges float; anemones squirt out water; and mosses and sea-weed shoot up.

And all kinds of plants spread out into branches, twist themselves into tendrils, lenghten into points, and grow round like fans. Pumpkins present the appearance of bosoms, and creeping plants entwine themselves like serpents.

The Dedaims of Babylon, which are trees, have as their fruits human heads; mandrakes sing; and the root Baaras runs into the grass.

And now the plants can no longer be distinguished from the animals. Polyparies, which have the appearance of sycamores, carry arms on their branches. Antony fancies he can trace a caterpillar between two leaves; it is a butterfly which flits away. He is on the point of walking over some shingle when up springs a grey grasshopper. Insects, like petals of roses, garnish a bush; the remains of ephemera make a bed of snow upon the soil.

And, next, the plants are indistinguishable from the stones.

Pebbles bear a resemblance to brains, stalactites to udders, and iron-dust to tapestries adorned with figures. In pieces of ice he can trace efflorescences, impressions of bushes and shells — so that one cannot tell whether they are the impressions of those objects or the objects themselves. Diamonds glisten like eyes, and minerals palpitate.

And he is no longer afraid! He lies down flat on his face, resting on his two elbows, and, holding in his breath, he gazes around.

Insects without stomachs keep eating; dried-up ferns begin to bloom afresh; and limbs which were wanting sprout forth again.

Finally, he perceives little globular bodies as large as pins' heads, and garnished all round with eyelashes. A vibration agitates them.

Antony, in ecstasy —

"O bliss! bliss! I have seen the birth of life; I have seen the beginning of motion. The blood beats so strongly in my veins that it seems about to burst them. I feel a longing to fly, to swim, to bark, to bellow, to howl. I would like to have wings, a tortoise-shell, a rind, to blow out smoke, to wear a trunk, to twist my body, to spread myself everywhere, to be in everything, to emanate with odours, to grow like plants, to flow like water, to vibrate like sound, to shine like light, to be outlined on every form, to penetrate every atom, to descend to the very depths of matter — to be matter!"

The dawn appears at last; and, like the uplifted curtains of a tabernacle, golden clouds, wreathing themselves into large volutes, reveal the sky.

In the very middle of it, and in the disc of the sun itself, shines the face of Jesus Christ.

Antony makes the sign of the Cross, and resumes his prayers.

Over Strand and Field

*A RECORD OF TRAVEL
THROUGH BRITTANY*

BY

GUSTAVE FLAUBERT

SIMON P. MAGEE
PUBLISHER
CHICAGO, ILL.

OVER STRAND AND FIELD*

A TRIP THROUGH BRITTANY

CHAPTER I.

CHÂTEAU DE CHAMBORD.

E WALKED through the empty galleries and deserted rooms where spiders spin their cobwebs over the salamanders of Francis the First. One is overcome by a feeling of distress at the sight of this poverty which has no grandeur. It is not absolute ruin, with the luxury of blackened and mouldy débris, the delicate embroidery of flowers, and the drapery of waving vines undulating in the breeze, like pieces of damask. It is a conscious poverty, for it brushes its threadbare coat and endeavours to appear respectable.

---

*Gustave Flaubert was twenty-six years old when he started on this journey. He travelled on foot and was accompanied by M. Maxime Ducamp. When they returned, they wrote an account of their journey. It is by far the most important of the unpublished writings, for in it the author gives his personal genius full sway and it abounds in picturesque descriptions and historical reflections.

The floor has been repaired in one room, while in the next it has been allowed to rot. It shows the futile effort to preserve that which is dying and to bring back that which has fled. Strange to say, it is all very melancholy, but not at all imposing.

And then it seems as if everything had contributed to injure poor Chambord, designed by Le Primatice and chiselled and sculptured by Germain Pilon and Jean Cousin. Upreared by Francis the First, on his return from Spain, after the humiliating treaty of Madrid (1526), it is the monument of a pride that sought to dazzle itself in order to forget defeat. It first harbours Gaston d'Orléans, a crushed pretender, who is exiled within its walls; then it is Louis XIV, who, out of one floor, builds three, thus ruining the beautiful double staircase which extended without interruption from the top to the bottom. Then one day, on the second floor, facing the front, under the magnificent ceiling covered with salamanders and painted ornaments which are now crumbling away, Molière produced for the first time *Le Bourgeois gentil-homme*. Then it was given to the Maréchal de Saxe; then to the Polignacs, and finally to a plain soldier, Berthier. It was afterwards bought back by subscription and presented to the Duc de Bordeaux. It has been given to everybody, as if nobody cared to have it or desired to keep it. It looks as if it had hardly ever been used, and as if it had always been too spacious. It is like a deserted hostelry where transient guests have not left even their names on the walls.

When we walked through an outside gallery to the Orléans staircase, in order to examine the caryatids which are supposed to represent Francis the First,

M. de Chateaubriand, and Madame d'Étampes, and turned around the celebrated lantern that terminates the big staircase, we stuck our heads several times through the railing to look down. In the courtyard was a little donkey nursing its mother, rubbing up against her, shaking its long ears and playfully jumping around. This is what we found in the court of honour of the Château de Chambord; these are its present hosts: a dog rolling in the grass, and a nursing, braying donkey frolicking on the threshold of kings!

Château d'Amboise.

The Château d'Amboise, which dominates the whole city that appears to be thrown at its feet like a mass of pebbles at the foot of a rock, looks like an imposing fortress, with its large towers pierced by long, narrow windows; its arched gallery that extends from the one to the other, and the brownish tint of its walls, darkened by the contrast of the flowers, which droop over them like a nodding plume on the bronzed forehead of an old soldier. We spent fully a quarter of an hour admiring the tower on the left; it is superb, imbrowned and yellowish in some places and coated with soot in others; it has charming charlocks hanging from its battlements, and is, in a word, one of those speaking monuments that seem to breathe and hold one spellbound and pensive under their gaze, like those paintings, the originals of which are unknown to us, but whom we love without knowing why.

The Château is reached by a slight incline which leads to a garden elevated like a terrace, from which the view extends on the whole surrounding country. It was of a delicate green; poplar trees lined the banks of the river; the meadows advanced to its edge, mingling their grey border with the bluish and vapourous horizon, vaguely enclosed by indistinct hills. The Loire flowed in the middle, bathing its islands, wetting the edge of the meadows, turning the wheels of the mills and letting the big boats glide peacefully, two by two, over its silvery surface, lulled to sleep by the creaking of the heavy rudders; and in the distance two big white sails gleamed in the sun.

Birds flew from the tops of the towers and the edge of the machicolations to some other spot, described circles in the air, chirped, and soon passed out of sight. About a hundred feet below us were the pointed roofs of the city, the empty courtyards of the old mansions, and the black holes of the smoky chimneys. Leaning in the niche of a battlement, we gazed and listened, and breathed it all in, enjoying the beautiful sunshine and balmy air impregnated with the pungent odour of the ruins. And there, without thinking of anything in particular, without even phrasing inwardly about something, I dreamed of coats of mail as pliable as gloves, of shields of buffalo hide soaked with sweat, of closed visors through which shot bloodthirsty glances, of wild and desperate night attacks with torches that set fire to the walls, and hatchets that mutilated the bodies; and of Louis XI, of the lover's war, of D'Aubigné and of the charlocks, the birds, the polished ivy, the denuded brambles, tasting in my pensive and idle occupation — what is greatest in men, their memory;— and what is most beautiful in nature, her ironical encroachments and eternal youth.

In the garden, among the lilac-bushes and the shrubs that droop over the alleys, rises the chapel, a work of the sixteenth century, chiselled at every angle, a perfect jewel, even more intricately decorated inside than out, cut out like the paper covering of a *bonbonnière*, and cunningly sculptured like the handle of a Chinese parasol. On the door is a *bas-relief* which is very amusing and ingenuous. It represents the meeting of Saint Hubert with the mystic stag, which bears a cross between its antlers. The saint is on his knees; above him hovers an angel who is about to place a crown on his cap; near them stands the saint's horse, watching the scene with a surprised expression; the dogs are barking and on the mountain, the sides and facets of which are cut to represent crystals, creeps the serpent. You can see its flat head advancing toward some leafless trees that look like cauliflowers. They are the sort of trees one comes upon in old Bibles, spare of foliage, thick and clumsy, bearing blossoms and fruit but no leaves; the symbolical, theological, and devout trees that are almost fantastical on account of their impossible ugliness. A little further, Saint Christopher is carrying Jesus on his shoulders; Saint Antony is in his cell, which is built on a rock; a pig is retiring into its hole and shows only its hind-quarters and its corkscrew tail, while a rabbit is sticking its head out of its house.

Of course, it is all a little clumsy and the moulding is not faultless. But there is so much life and movement about the figure and the animals, so much charm in the details, that one would give a great deal to be able to carry it away and take it home.

Inside of the Château, the insipid Empire style is

reproduced in every apartment.   Almost every room
is adorned with busts of Louis-Philippe and Madame
Adélaïde.   The present reigning family has a craze
for being portrayed on canvas.   It is the bad taste of
a parvenu, the mania of a grocer who has accumulated money and who enjoys seeing himself in red,
white, and yellow, with his watch-charms dangling
over his stomach, his bewhiskered chin and his children gathered around him.

On one of the towers, and in spite of the most ordinary common sense, they have built a glass rotunda
which is used for a dining-room.   True, the view
from it is magnificent.   But the building presents
so shocking an appearance from the outside, that one
would, I should think, prefer to see nothing of the
environs, or else to eat in the kitchen.

In order to go back to the city, we came down
by a tower that was used by carriages to approach
the Château.   The sloping gravelled walk turns around
a stone axle like the steps of a staircase.   The arch is
dark and lighted only by the rays that creep through
the loop-holes.   The columns on which the interior
end of the vault rests, are decorated with grotesque
or vulgar subjects.   A dogmatic intention seems to
have presided over their composition.   It would be
well for travellers to begin the inspection at the bottom, with the *Aristoteles equitatus* (a subject which
has already been treated on one of the choir statues
in the Cathedral of Rouen) and reach by degrees a pair
embracing in the manner which both Lucretius and
l'Amour Conjugal have recommended.   The greater
part of the intermediary subjects have been removed,
to the despair of seekers of comical things, like ourselves; they have been removed in cold blood, with

deliberate intent, for the sake of decency, and because, as one of the servants of his Majesty informed us convincingly, "a great many were improper for the lady visitors to see."

Château de Chenonceaux.

A something of infinite suavity and aristocratic serenity pervades the Château de Chenonceaux. It is situated outside of the village, which keeps at a respectful distance. It can be seen through a large avenue of trees, and is enclosed by woods and an extensive park with beautiful lawns. Built on the water, it proudly uprears its turrets and its square chimneys. The Cher flows below, and murmurs at the foot of its arches, the pointed corners of which form eddies in the tide. It is all very peaceful and charming, graceful yet robust. Its calm is not wearying and its melancholy has no tinge of bitterness.

One enters through the end of a long, arched hallway, which used to be a fencing-room. It is decorated with some armours, which, in spite of the obvious necessity of their presence, do not shock one's taste or appear out of place. The whole scheme of interior decoration is tastefully carried out; the furniture and hangings of the period have been preserved and cared for intelligently. The great, venerable mantel-pieces of the sixteenth century do not shelter the hideous and economical German stoves, which might easily be hidden in some of them.

In the kitchen, situated in a wing of the castle, which we visited later, a maid was peeling vegetables and a scullion was washing dishes, while the cook was standing in front of the stove, superintending a reasonable number of shining saucepans. It was all very delightful, and bespoke the idle and intelligent home life of a gentleman. I like the owners of Chenonceaux.

In fact, have you not often seen charming old paintings that make you gaze at them indefinitely, because they portray the period in which their owners lived, the ballets in which the farthingales of all those beautiful pink ladies whirled around, and the sword-thrusts which those noblemen gave each other with their rapiers? Here are some temptations of history. One would like to know whether those people loved as we do, and what difference existed between their passions and our own. One would like them to open their lips and tell their history, tell us everything they used to do, no matter how futile, and what their cares and pleasures used to be. It is an irritating and seductive curiosity, a dreamy desire for knowledge, such as one feels regarding the past life of a mistress. . . . But they are deaf to the questions our eyes put to them, they remain dumb and motionless in their wooden frames, and we pass on. The moths attack their canvases, but the latter are revarnished; and the pictures will smile on when we are buried and forgotten. And others will come and gaze upon them, till the day they crumble to dust; then people will dream in the same old way before our own likenesses, and ask themselves what used to happen in our day, and whether life was not more alluring then.

I should not have spoken again of those handsome dames, if the large, full-length portrait of Madame Deshoulières, in an elaborate white *déshabille,* (it was really a fine picture, and, like the much decried and seldom read efforts of the poetess, better at the second look than at the first), had not reminded me, by the expression of the mouth, which is large, full, and sensual, of the peculiar coarseness of Madame de Staël's portrait by Gérard. When I saw it two years ago, at Coppet, in bright sunshine, I could not help being impressed by those red, vinous lips and the wide, aspiring nostrils. George Sand's face offers a similar peculiarity. In all those women who were half masculine, spirituality revealed itself only in the eyes. All the rest remained material.

In point of amusing incidents, there is still at Chenonceaux, in Diane de Poitiers's room, the wide canopy bedstead of the royal favourite, done in white and red. If it belonged to me, it would be very hard for me not to use it once in a while. To sleep in the bed of Diane de Poitiers, even though it be empty, is worth as much as sleeping in that of many more palpable realities. Moreover, has it not been said that all the pleasure in these things was only imagination? Then, can you conceive of the peculiar and historical voluptuousness, for one who possesses some imagination, to lay his head on the pillow that belonged to the mistress of Francis the First, and to stretch his limbs on her mattress? (Oh! how willingly I would give all the women in the world for the mummy of Cleopatra!) But I would not dare to touch, for fear of breaking them, the porcelains belonging to Catherine de Médicis, in the dining-room, nor place my foot in the stirrup of Francis the First, for fear it might remain there, nor put my lips to the mouth-piece of the huge trumpet in the fencing-room, for fear of rupturing my lungs.

CHAPTER II.

ON A hill at the foot of which two rivers mingle their waters, in a fresh landscape, brightened by the light colours of the inclined roofs, that are grouped like many sketches of Hubert, near a waterfall that turns the wheel of a mill hidden among the leaves, the Château de Clisson raises its battered roof above the tree-tops. Everything around it is calm and peaceful. The little dwellings seem to smile as if they had been built under softer skies; the waters sing their song, and patches of moss cover a stream over which hang graceful clusters of foliage. The horizon extends on one side into a tapering perspective of meadows, while on the other it rises abruptly and is enclosed by a wooded valley, the trees of which crowd together and form a green ocean.

After one crosses the bridge and arrives at the steep path which leads to the Château, one sees, standing upreared and bold on the moat on which it is built, a formidable wall, crowned with battered machicolations and bedecked with trees and ivy, the luxuriant growth of which covers the grey stones and sways in the wind, like an immense green veil which the recumbent giant moves dreamily across his shoulders. The grass is tall and dark, the plants are strong and hardy; the trunks of the ivy are twisted, knotted, and rough, and lift up the walls as with levers or hold them in the network of their branches. In one spot, a tree has grown through the wall horizontally, and, suspended in the air, has let its branches radiate around it. The moats, the steep slope of which is broken by the earth which has detached itself from the embankments and the stones which have fallen from the battlements, have a wide, deep curve, like hatred and pride; and the portal, with its strong, slightly arched ogive, and its two bays that raise the drawbridge, looks like a great helmet with holes in its visor.

When one enters, he is surprised and astonished at the wonderful mixture of ruins and trees, the ruins accentuating the freshness of the trees, while the latter in turn, render more poignant the melancholy of the ruins. Here, indeed, is the beautiful, eternal, and brilliant laughter of nature over the skeleton of things; here is the insolence of her wealth and the deep grace of her encroachments, and the melodious invasions of her silence. A grave and pensive enthusiasm fills one's soul; one feels that the sap flows in the trees and that the grass grows with the same strength and the same rhythm, as the stones crumble and the walls cave in. A sublime art, in the supreme accord of secondary discordances, has contrasted the unruly ivy with the sinuous sweep of the ruins, the brambles with the heaps of crumbling stones, the clearness of the atmosphere with the strong projections of the masses, the colour of the sky with the colour of the earth, reflecting each one in the other: that which was, and that which is. Thus history and nature always reveal, though they may accomplish it in a circumscribed spot of the world, the unceasing relation, the eternal hymen of dying humanity and the growing daisy; of the stars that glow, and the men who expire, of the heart that beats and the wave that rises. And this is so clearly indicated here, is so overwhelming, that one shudders inwardly, as if this dual life centred in one's own body; so brutal and immediate is the perception of these harmonies and developments. For the eye also has its orgies and the mind its delights.

At the foot of two large trees, the trunks of which are intersected, a stream of light floods the grass and seems like a luminous river, brightening the solitude. Overhead, a dome of leaves, through which one can see the sky presenting a vivid contrast of blue, reverberates a bright, greenish light, which illuminates the ruins, accentuating the deep furrows, intensifying the shadows, and disclosing all the hidden beauties. You advance and walk between those walls and under the trees, wander along the barbicans, pass under the falling arcades from which spring large, waving plants. The vaults, which contain corpses, echo under your footfalls; lizards run in the grass, beetles creep along the walls, the sky is blue, and the sleepy ruins pursue their dream.

With its triple enclosure, its dungeons, its interior court-yards, its machicolations, its underground passages, its ramparts piled one upon the other, like a bark on a bark and a shield on a shield, the ancient Château of the Clissons rises before your mind and is reconstructed. The memory of past existences exudes from its walls with the emanations of the nettles and the coolness of the ivy. In that castle, men altogether different from us were swayed by passions stronger than ours; their hands were brawnier and their chests broader.

Long black streaks still mark the walls, as in the time when logs blazed in the eighteen-foot fireplaces. Symmetrical holes in the masonry indicate the floors to which one ascended by winding staircases now crumbling in ruins, while their empty doors open into space. Sometimes a bird, taking flight from its nest hanging in the branches, would pass with spread wings through the arch of a window, and fly far away into the country.

At the top of a high, bleak wall, several square bay-windows, of unequal length and position, let the pure sky shine through their crossed bars; and the bright blue, framed by the stone, attracted my eye with surprising persistency. The sparrows in the trees were chirping, and in the midst of it all a cow, thinking, no doubt, that it was a meadow, grazed peacefully, her horns sweeping over the grass.

There is a window, a large window that looks out into a meadow called *la prairie des chevaliers*. It was there, from a stone bench carved in the wall, that the high-born dames of the period watched the knights urge their iron-barbed steeds against one another, and the lances come down on the helmets and snap, and the men fall to the ground. On a fine summer day, like to-day, perhaps, when the mill that enlivens the whole landscape did not exist, when there were roofs on the walls, and Flemish hangings, and oil-cloths on the window-sills, when there was less grass, and when human voices and rumours filled the air, more than one heart beat with love and anguish under its red velvet bodice. Beautiful white hands twitched with fear on the stone, which is now covered with moss, and the embroidered veils of high caps fluttered in the wind that plays with my cravat and that swayed the plumes of the knights.

We went down into the vaults where Jean V was imprisoned. In the men's dungeon we saw the large double hook that was used for executions; and we touched curiously with our fingers the door of the women's prison. It is about four inches thick and is plated with heavy iron bars. In the middle is a little grating that was used to throw in whatever was necessary to prevent the captive from starving. It was this grating which opened instead of the door, which, being the mouth of the most terrible confessions, was one of those that always closed but never opened. In those days there was real hatred. If you hated a person. and he had been kidnapped by surprise or traitorously trapped in an interview, and was in your power, you could torture him at your own sweet will. Every minute, every hour, you could delight in his anguish and drink his tears. You could go down into his cell and speak to him and bargain with him, laugh at his tortures, and discuss his ransom; you could live on and off him, through his slowly ebbing life and his plundered treasures. Your whole castle, from the top of the towers to the bottom of the trenches, weighed on him, crushing and burying him; and thus family revenges were accomplished by the family itself, a fact which constituted their potency and symbolised the idea.

Sometimes, however, when the wretched prisoner was an aristocrat and a wealthy man, and he was

near death, and one was tired of him, and his tears
had acted upon the hatred of his master like refresh-
ing bleedings, there was talk of releasing him. The
captive promised everything; he would return the
fortified towns, hand over the keys to his best cities,
give his daughter in marriage, endow churches and
journey on foot to the Holy Sepulchre. And money!
Money! Why, he would have more of it coined by
the Jews! Then the treaty would be signed and
dated and counter-signed; the relics would be brought
forth to be sworn on, and the prisoner would be a
free man once more. He would jump on his horse,
gallop away, and when he reached home he would
order the drawbridge hoisted, call his vassals together,
and take down his sword from the wall. His hatred
would find an outlet in terrific explosions of wrath.
It was the time of frightful passions and victorious
rages. The oath? The Pope would free him from it,
and the ransom he simply ignored.

When Clisson was imprisoned in the Château de
l'Hermine, he promised for his freedom a hundred
thousand francs' worth of gold, the restitution of the
towns belonging to the duke of Penthièvre, and the
cancelling of his daughter Marguerite's betrothal to
the Duke of Penthièvre. But as soon as he was set
free, he began by attacking Chateladren, Guingamp,
Lamballe and St. Malo, which cities either were taken
or they capitulated. But the people of Brittany paid
for the fun.

When Jean V. was captured by the Count of Penthièvre at the bridge of Loroux, he promised a ransom of one million; he promised his eldest daughter,
who was already betrothed to the King of Sicily.
He promised Montcontour, Sesson and Jugan, etc.,

7—1.

but he gave neither his daughter nor the money, nor the cities. He had promised to go to the Holy Sepulchre. He acquitted himself of this by proxy. He had taken an oath that he would no longer levy taxes and subsidies. The Pope freed him from this pledge. He had promised to give Nôtre-Dame de Nantes his weight in gold; but as he weighed nearly two hundred pounds, he remained greatly indebted. With all that he was able to pick up or snatch away, he quickly formed a league and compelled the house of Penthièvre to buy the peace which they had sold to him.

On the other side of the Sèvre, a forest covers the hill with its fresh, green maze of trees; it is *La Garenne,* a park that is beautiful in itself, in spite of the artificial embellishments that have been introduced. M. Semot, (the father of the present owner), was a painter of the Empire and a laureate, and he tried to reproduce to the best of his ability that cold Italian, republican, Roman style. which was so popular in the time of Canova and of Madame de Staël. In those days people were inclined to be pompous and noble. They used to place chiselled urns on graves and paint everybody in a flowing cloak, and with long hair; then Corinne sang to the accompaniment of her lyre beside Oswald, who wore Russian boots; and it was thought proper to have everybody's head adorned with a profusion of dishevelled locks and to have a multitude of ruins in every landscape.

This style of embellishment abounds throughout La Garenne. There is a temple erected to Vesta, and directly opposite it another erected to Friendship. . . .

Inscriptions, artificial rocks, factitious ruins, are scattered lavishly, with artlessness and conviction.

. . . But the poetical riches centre in the grotto of Héloïse, a sort of natural dolmen on the bank of the Sèvre.

Why have people made Héloïse, who was such a great and noble figure, appear commonplace and silly, the prototype of all crossed loves and the narrow ideal of sentimental schoolgirls? The unfortunate mistress of the great Abélard deserved a better fate, for she loved him with devoted admiration, although he was hard and taciturn at times and spared her neither bitterness nor blows. She dreaded offending him more than she dreaded offending God, and strove harder to please him. She did not wish him to marry her, because she thought that "it was wrong and deplorable that the one whom nature had created for all . . . should be appropriated by one woman." She found, she said, "more happiness in the appellation of mistress or concubine, than in that of wife or empress," and by humiliating herself in him, she hoped to gain a stronger hold over his heart.

The park is really delightful. Alleys wind through the woods and clusters of trees bend over the meandering stream. You can hear the bubbling water and feel the coolness of the foliage. If we were irritated by the bad taste displayed here, it was because we had just left Clisson, which has a real, simple, and solid beauty, and after all, this bad taste is not that of our contemporaries. But what is, in fact, bad taste? Invariably it is the taste of the period which has preceded ours. Bad taste at the time of Ronsard was represented by Marot; at the time of Boileau, by Ronsard; at the time of Voltaire, by Corneille, and by Voltaire in the day of Chateaubriand, whom many people nowadays begin to think a trifle weak. O men of taste in future centuries, let me recommend you the men of taste of to-day! You will laugh at their cramps, their superb disdain, their preference for veal and milk, and the faces they make when underdone meat and too ardent poetry is served to them. Everything that is beautiful will then appear ugly; everything that is graceful, stupid; everything that is rich, poor; and oh! how our delightful boudoirs, our charming salons, our exquisite costumes, our palpitating plays, our interesting novels, our serious books will all be consigned to the garret or be used for old paper and manure! O posterity, above all things do not forget our gothic salons, our Renaissance furniture, M. Pasquier's discourses, the shape of our hats, and the æsthetics of *La Revue des Deux Mondes!*

While we were pondering upon these lofty philosophical considerations, our wagon had hauled us over to Tiffanges. Seated side by side in a sort of tin tub, our weight crushed the tiny horse, which swayed to and fro between the shafts. It was like the twitching of an eel in the body of a musk-rat. Going down hill pushed him forward, going up hill pulled him backward, while uneven places in the road threw him from side to side, and the wind and the whip lashed him alternately. The poor brute! I cannot think of him now without a certain feeling of remorse.

The road down hill is curved and its edges are covered with clumps of sea-rushes or large patches of a certain reddish moss. To the right, on an eminence that starts from the bottom of the dale and swells in the middle like the carapace of a tortoise, one perceives high, unequal walls, the crumbling tops of which appear one above another.

One follows a hedge, climbs a path, and enters an open portal which has sunken into the ground to the depth of one third of its ogive. The men who used to pass through it on horseback would be obliged to bend over their saddles in order to enter it to-day. When the earth is tired of supporting a monument, it swells up underneath it, creeps up to it like a wave, and while the sky causes the top to crumble away, the ground obliterates the foundations. The court-yard was deserted and the calm water that filled the moats remained motionless and flat under the pond-lilies.

The sky was white and cloudless, but without sunshine. Its bleak curve extended far away, cover-ing the country with a cold and cheerless monotony. Not a sound could be heard, the birds did not sing, even the horizon was mute, and from the empty fur-rows came neither the scream of the crows as they soar heavenward, nor the soft creaking of plough-wheels. We climbed down through brambles and underbrush into a deep and dark trench, hidden at the foot of a large tower, which stands in the water surrounded by reeds. A lone window opens on one side: a dark square relieved by the grey line of its stone cross-bar. A capricious cluster of wild honeysuckle covers the sill, and its maze of perfumed blossoms creeps along the walls. When one looks up, the openings of the big machicolations reveal only a part of the sky, or some little, unknown flower which has nestled in the bat-tlement, its seed having been wafted there on a stormy day and left to sprout in the cracks of the stones.

Presently, a long, balmy breeze swept over us like a sigh, and the trees in the moats, the moss on the stones, the reeds in the water, the plants among the ruins, and the ivy, which covered the tower from top to bottom with a layer of shining leaves, all trembled and shook their foliage; the corn in the fields rippled in endless waves that again and again bent the swaying tops of the ears; the pond wrinkled and welled up against the foot of the tower; the leaves of the ivy all quivered at once, and an apple-tree in bloom covered the ground with pink blossoms.

Nothing, nothing! The open sky, the growing grass, the passing wind. No ragged child tending a browsing cow; not even, as elsewhere, some solitary goat sticking its shaggy head through an aperture in the walls to turn at our approach and flee in terror through the bushes; not a song-bird, not a nest, not a sound! This castle is like a ghost: mute and cold, it stands abandoned in this deserted place, and looks accursed and replete with terrifying recollections. Still, this melancholy dwelling, which the owls now seem to avoid, was once inhabited. In the dungeon, between four walls as livid as the bottom of an old drinking-trough, we were able to discover the traces of five floors. A chimney, with its two round pillars and black top, has remained suspended in the air at a height of thirty feet. Earth has accumulated on it, and plants are growing there as if it were a jardinière.

Beyond the second enclosure, in a ploughed field, one can recognise the ruins of a chapel by the broken shafts of an ogive portal. Grass has grown around it, and trees have replaced the columns. Four hundred years ago, this chapel was filled with ornaments of gold cloth and silk, censers, chandeliers, chalices, crosses, precious stones, gold vessels and vases, a choir of thirty singers, chaplains, musicians, and children sang hymns to the accompaniment of an organ which they took along with them when they travelled. They were clad in scarlet garments lined with pearl grey and vair. There was one whom they called archdeacon, and another whom they called bishop, and the Pope was asked to allow them to wear mitres like canons, for this chapel was the chapel, and this castle one of the castles of Gilles de Laval, lord of Rouci, of Montmorency, of Retz and of Craon, lieutenant-general of the Duke of Brittany and field-marshal of France, who was burned at Nantes on the 25th of October, 1440, in the Prée de la Madéleine for being a counterfeiter, a murderer, a magician, an atheist and a Sodomite.

He possessed more than one hundred thousand crowns' worth of furniture; an income of thirty thousand pounds a year, the profits of his fiefs and his salary as field-marshal; fifty magnificently appointed horsemen escorted him. He kept open house, served the rarest viands and the oldest wines at his board, and gave representations of mysteries, as cities used to do when a king was within their gates. When his money gave out, he sold his estates; when those were gone, he looked around for more gold, and when he had destroyed his furnaces, he called on the devil. He wrote him that he would give him all that he possessed, excepting his life and his soul. He made sacrifices, gave alms and instituted ceremonies in his honour. At night, the bleak walls of the castle lighted up by the glare of the torches that flared amid bumpers of rare wines and gipsy jugglers, and blushed hotly under the unceasing breath of magical bellows. The inhabitants invoked the devil, joked with death, murdered children, enjoyed frightful and atrocious pleasures; blood flowed, instruments played, everything echoed with voluptuousness, horror, and madness.

When he expired, four or five damsels had his body removed from the stake, laid out, and taken to the Carmelites, who, after performing the customary services, buried him in state.

On one of the bridges of the Loire, relates Guépin, opposite the Hôtel de la Boule-d'Or, an expiatory monument was erected to his memory. It was a niche containing the statue of the *Bonne Vierge de crée lait,* who had the power of creating milk in nurses; the good people offered her butter and similar rustic products. The niche still exists, but the statue is gone; the same as at the town-house, where the casket which contained the heart of Queen Anne is also empty. But we did not care to see the casket; we did not even give it a thought. I should have preferred gazing upon the trousers of the marshal of Retz to looking at the heart of Madame Anne de Bretagne.

CHAPTER III.

CARNAC.

THE field of Carnac is a large, open space where eleven rows of black stones are aligned at symmetrical intervals. They diminish in size as they recede from the ocean. Cambry asserts that there were four thousand of these rocks and Fréminville has counted twelve hundred of them. They are certainly very numerous.

What was their use? Was it a temple?

One day Saint Cornille, pursued along the shore by soldiers, was about to jump into the ocean, when he thought of changing them all into stone, and forthwith the men were petrified. But this explanation was good only for fools, little children, and poets. Other people looked for better reasons.

In the sixteenth century, Olaüs Magnus, archbishop of Upsal (who, banished to Rome, wrote a book on the antiquities of his country that met with widespread success except in his native land, Sweden, where it was not translated), discovered that, when these stones form one long, straight row, they cover the bodies of warriors who died while fighting duels;

that those arranged in squares are consecrated to heroes that perished in battle; that those disposed in a circle are family graves, while those that form corners or angular figures are the tombs of horsemen or foot-soldiers, and more especially of those fighters whose party had triumphed. All this is quite clear, but Olaüs Magnus has forgotten to tell us how two cousins who killed each other in a duel on horseback could have been buried. The fact of the duel required that the stones be straight; the relationship required that they be circular; but as the men were horsemen, it seems as if the stones ought to have been arranged squarely, though this rule, it is true, was not formal, as it was applied only to those whose party had triumphed. O good Olaüs Magnus! You must have liked Monte-Pulciano exceeding well! And how many draughts of it did it take for you to acquire all this wonderful knowledge?

According to a certain English doctor named Borlase, who had observed similar stones in Cornouailles, "they buried soldiers there, in the very place where they died." As if, usually, they were carted to the cemetery! And he builds his hypothesis on the following comparison: their graves are on a straight line, like the front of an army on plains that were the scene of some great action.

Then they tried to bring in the Greeks, the Egyptians, and the Cochin Chinese! There is a Karnac in Egypt, they said, and one on the coast of Brittany. Now, it is probable that this Karnac descends from the Egyptian one; it is quite certain! In Egypt they are sphinxes; here they are rocks; but in both instances they are of stone. So it would seem that the Egyptians (who never travelled), came to this coast (of the existence of which they were ignorant), founded a colony (they never founded any), and left these crude statues (they produced such beautiful ones), as a positive proof of their sojourn in this country (which nobody mentions).

People fond of mythology thought them the columns of Hercules; people fond of natural history thought them a representation of the python, because, according to Pausanias, a similar heap of stones, on the road from Thebes to Elissonte, was called "the serpent's head," and especially because the rows of stones at Carnac present the sinuosities of a serpent. People fond of cosmography discovered a zodiac, like M. de Cambry, who recognised in those eleven rows of stones the twelve signs of the zodiac, "for it must be stated," he adds, "that the ancient Gauls had only eleven signs to the zodiac."

Subsequently, a member of the Institute conjectured that it might perhaps be the cemetery of the Venetians, who inhabited Vannes, situated six miles from Carnac, and who founded Venice, as everybody knows. Another man wrote that these Venetians, conquered by Cæsar, erected all those rocks solely in a spirit of humility and in order to honour their victor. But people were getting tired of the cemetery theory, the serpent and the zodiac; they set out again and this time found a Druidic temple.

The few documents that we possess, scattered through Pliny and Dionysius Cassius, agree in stating that the Druids chose dark places for their ceremonies, like the depths of the woods with "their vast silence." And as Carnac is situated on the coast, and surrounded by a barren country, where nothing but these gentlemen's fancies has ever grown, the first grenadier of France, but not, in my estimation, the cleverest man, followed by Pelloutier and by M. Mahé, (canon of the cathedral of Vannes), concluded that it was "a Druidic temple in which political meetings must also have been held."

But all had not been said, and it still remained to be discovered of what use the empty spaces in the rows could have been. "Let us look for the reason, a thing nobody has ever thought of before," cried M. Mahé, and, quoting a sentence from Pomponius Mela: "The Druids teach the nobility many things and instruct them secretly in caves and forests;" and this one from Tucain: "You dwell in tall forests," he reached the conclusion that the Druids not only officiated at the sanctuaries, but that they also lived and taught in them. "So the monument of Carnac being a sanctuary, like the Gallic forests, (O power of induction! where are you leading Father Mahé, canon of Vannes and correspondent of the Academy of Agriculture at Poitiers?), there is reason to believe that the intervals, which break up the rows of stones, held rows of houses where the Druids lived with their families and numerous pupils, and where the heads of the nation, who, on state days, betook themselves to the sanctuary, found comfortable lodgings. Good old Druids! Excellent ecclesiastics! How they have been calumnied! They lived there so righteously with their families and numerous pupils, and even were amiable enough to prepare lodgings for the principals of the nation!

But at last came a man imbued with the genius of ancient things and disdainful of trodden paths. He was able to recognize the rests of a Roman camp, and, strangely enough, the rests of one of the camps of

Cæsar, who had had these stones upreared only to
serve as support for the tents of his soldiers and prevent them from being blown away by the wind.
What gales there must have been in those days, on
the coasts of Armorica!

The honest writer who, to the glory of the great
Julius, discovered this sublime precaution, (thus returning to Cæsar that which never belonged to Cæsar),
was a former pupil of l'École Polytechnique, an engineer, a M. de la Sauvagère. The collection of all
these data constitutes what is called *Celtic Archæ-
ology*, the mysteries of which we shall presently disclose.

A stone placed on another one is called a "dolmen,"
whether it be horizontal or perpendicular. A group
of upright stones covered by succeeding flat stones,
and forming a series of dolmens, is a "fairy grotto,"
a "fairy rock," a "devil's stable," or a "giant's
palace"; for, like the people who serve the same
wine under different labels, the Celto-maniacs, who
had almost nothing to offer, decorated the same
things with various names. When these stones form
an ellipse, and have no head-covering, one must say:
There is a "cromlech"; when one perceives a stone
laid horizontally upon two upright stones, one is confronted by a "lichaven" or a "trilithe." Often two
enormous rocks are put one on top of the other, and
touch only at one point, and we read that "they are
balanced in such a way that the wind alone is sufficient to make the upper rock sway perceptibly," an
assertion which I do not dispute, although I am
rather suspicious of the Celtic wind, and although
these swaying rocks have always remained unshaken
in spite of the fierce kicks I was artless enough to

give them; they are called "rolling or rolled stones,"
"turned or transported stones," "stones that dance
or dancing stones," "stones that twist or twisting
stones." You must still learn what a *pierre fichade,*
a *pierre fiche,* a *pierre fixée* are, and what is meant
by a *haute borne,* a *pierre latte* and a *pierre lait;* in
what a *pierre fonte* differs from a *pierre fiette,* and
what connection there is between a *chaire à diable*
and a *pierre droite;* then you will be as wise as ever
were Pelloutier, Déric, Latour d'Auvergne, Penhoet
and others, not forgetting Mahé and Fréminville. Now,
all this means a *pulvan,* also called a *men-hir,* and
designates nothing more than a stone of greater or
lesser size, placed by itself in an open field.

I was about to forget the tumuli! Those that are
composed of silica and soil are called "barrows" in
high-flown language, while the simple heaps of
stones are "gals-gals."

People have pretended that when they were not
tombs the "dolmens" and "trilithes" were altars, that
the "fairy rocks" were assembling places or sepultures,
and that the business meetings at the time of the Druids
were held in the "cromlechs." M. de Cambry saw in
the "swaying rocks" the emblems of the suspended
world. The "barrows" and "gals-gals" have undoubtedly been tombs; and as for the "men-hirs,"
people went so far as to pretend that they had a
form which led to the deduction that a certain cult
reigned throughout lower Brittany. O chaste immod-
esty of science, you respect nothing, not even a
peulven!

A reverie, no matter how undefined, may lead up
to splendid creations, when it starts from a fixed
point. Then the imagination, like a soaring hippo-

griff, stamps the earth with all its might and journeys straightway towards infinite regions. But when it applies itself to a subject devoid of plastic art and history, and tries to extract a science from it, and to reconstruct a world, it remains even poorer and more barren than the rough stone to which the vanity of some praters has lent a shape and dignified with a history.

To return to the stones of Carnac (or rather, to leave them), if anyone should, after all these opinions, ask me mine, I would emit an irresistible, irrefutable, incontestable one, which would make the tents of M. de la Sauvagère stagger, blanch the face of the Egyptian Penhoët, break up the zodiac of Cambry and smash the python into a thousand bits. This is my opinion: the stones of Carnac are simply large stones!

So we returned to the inn and dined heartily, for our five hours' tramp had sharpened our appetites. We were served by the hostess, who had large blue eyes, delicate hands, and the sweet face of a nun. It was not yet bedtime, and it was too dark to work, so we went to the church.

This is small, although it has a nave and side-aisles like a city church. Short, thick stone pillars support its wooden roof, painted in blue, from which hang miniature vessels, votive offerings that were promised during raging storms. Spiders creep along their sails and the riggings are rotting under the dust. No service was being held, and the lamp in the choir burned dimly in its cup filled with yellow oil; overhead, through the open windows of the darkened vault, came broad rays of white light and the sound of the wind rustling in the tree-tops. A man came in to put the chairs in order, and placed two candles in an iron chandelier riveted to the stone pillar; then he pulled into the middle of the aisle a sort of stretcher with a pedestal, its black wood stained with large white spots. Other people entered the church, and a priest clad in his surplice passed us. There was the intermittent tinkling of a bell and then the door of the church opened wide. The jangling sound of the little bell mingled with the tones of another and their sharp, clear tones swelled louder as they came nearer and nearer to us.

A cart drawn by oxen appeared and halted in front of the church. It held a corpse, whose dull white feet protruded from under the winding-sheet like bits of washed alabaster, while the body itself had the uncertain form peculiar to dressed corpses. The crowd around was silent. The men bared their heads; the priest shook his holy-water sprinkler and mumbled orisons, and the pair of oxen swung their heads to and fro under the heavy, creaking yoke. The church, in the background of which gleamed a star, formed one huge shadow in the greenish outdoor atmosphere of a rainy twilight, and the child who held a light on the threshold had to keep his hand in front of it to prevent the wind from blowing it out.

They lifted the body from the cart, and in doing so struck its head against the pole. They carried it into the church and placed it on the stretcher. A crowd of men and women followed. They knelt on the floor, the men near the corpse, and the women a little farther away, near the door; then the service began.

It did not last very long, at least it impressed us that way, for the low psalmodies were recited rapidly and drowned now and then by a stifled sob which came from under the black hoods near the door. A hand touched me and I drew aside to let a bent woman pass. With her clenched fists on her breast, and face averted, she advanced without appearing to move her feet, eager to see, yet trembling to behold, and reached the row of lights which burned beside the bier. Slowly, very slowly, lifting up her arm as if to hide herself under it, she turned her head on her shoulder and sank in a heap on a chair, as limp as her garments.

By the light of the candles, I could see her staring eyes, framed by lids that looked as if they had been scalded, so red were they; her idiotic and contracted mouth, trembling with despair, and her whole pitiful face. which was drenched with tears.

The corpse was that of her husband, who had been lost at sea; he had been washed ashore and was now being laid to rest.

The cemetery adjoined the church. The mourners passed into it through a side-door, while the corpse was being nailed in its coffin, in the vestry. A fine rain moistened the atmosphere; we felt cold; the earth was slippery and the grave-diggers who had not completed their task. found it hard to raise the heavy soil, for it stuck to their shovels. In the background, the women kneeling in the grass, throwing back their hoods and their big white caps, the starched wings of which fluttered in the wind, appeared at a distance like an immense winding-sheet hovering over the earth.

When the corpse reappeared, the prayers began again, and the sobs broke out anew, and could be heard through the dropping rain.

Not far from us, issued, at regular intervals, a sort of subdued gurgle that sounded like laughter. In any other place, a person hearing it would have thought it the repressed explosion of some overwhelming joy or the paroxysm of a delirious happiness. It was the widow, weeping. Then she walked to the edge of the grave, as did the rest of the mourners, and little by little, the soil assumed its ordinary level and everybody went home.

As we walked down the cemetery steps, a young fellow passed us and said in French to a companion: "Heavens! didn't the fellow stink! He is almost completely mortified! It isn't surprising, though, after being in the water three weeks!"

One morning we started as on other mornings; we chose the same road, and passed the hedge of young elms and the sloping meadow where the day before we had seen a little girl chasing cattle to the drinking-trough; but it was the last day, and the last time perhaps, that we should pass that way.

A muddy stretch of land, into which we sank up to our ankles, extends from Carnac to the village of Pô. A boat was waiting for us; we entered it, and they hoisted the sail and pushed off. Our sailor, an old man with a cheerful face, sat aft; he fastened a line to the gunwale and let his peaceful boat go its own way. There was hardly any wind; the blue sea was calm and the narrow track the rudder ploughed in the waters could be seen for a long time. The old fellow was talkative; he spoke of the priests, whom he disliked, of meat, which he thought was a good thing to eat even on fast days, of the work he had had when he was in the navy, and of the shots

he had received when he was a customs officer.
. . . The boat glided along slowly, the line followed us and the end of the *tape-cul* hung in the water.

The mile we had to walk in order to go from Saint-Pierre to Quiberon was quickly covered, in spite of a hilly and sandy road, and the sun, which made our shoulders smart beneath the straps of our bags, and a number of "men-hirs" that were scattered along the route.

CHAPTER IV.

QUIBERON.

N QUIBERON, we breakfasted at old Rohan Belle-Isle's, who keeps the Hôtel Penthièvre. This gentleman had his bare feet stuck in old slippers, on account of the heat, and was drinking with a mason, a fact which does not prevent him from being the descendant of one of the first families of Europe; an aristocrat of the old stock! a real aristocrat! *Vive Dieu!* He immediately set to work to pound a steak and to cook us some lobsters. Our pride was flattered to its innermost fibre.

The past of Quiberon is concentrated in a massacre. Its greatest curiosity is a cemetery, which is filled to its utmost capacity and overflows into the street. The head-stones are crowded together and invade and submerge one another, as if the corpses were uncomfortable in their graves and had lifted up their shoulders to escape from them. It suggests a petrified ocean, the tombs being the waves, and the crosses the masts of shipwrecked vessels.

In the middle, an open ossuary contains skeletons that have been exhumed in order to make room for other corpses. Who has said: "Life is a hostelry, and the grave is our home?" But these corpses do not remain in their graves, for they are only tenants and are ejected at the expiration of the lease. Around this charnel-house, where the heaps of bones resemble a mass of fagots, is arranged, breast-high, a series of little black boxes, six inches square, surmounted by a cross and cut out in the shape of a heart in front, so that one can see the skulls inside. Above the heart-shaped opening are the following words in painted letters: "This is the head of ——— ——, deceased on such and such a day, in such and such a year." These heads belonged to persons of a certain standing, and one would be considered an ungrateful son if, after seven years, he did not give his parents' skulls the luxury of one of these little black boxes. The remainder of the bodies is thrown into the bone-house, and twenty-five years afterwards the heads are sent to join them. A few years ago they tried to abolish the custom; but a riot ensued and the practice continued.

Perhaps it is wicked to play with those round skulls which once contained a mind, with those empty circles in which passion throbbed. Those boxes surrounding the ossuary and scattered over the graves, over the wall and in the grass, without any attempt at order, may appear horrible to a few and ridiculous to many; but those black cases rotting even as the bones blanch and crumble to dust; those skulls, with noses eaten away and foreheads streaked by the slimy trails of snails, and hollow, staring eyes; those thigh-bones piled up as in the great charnel-houses mentioned in the Bible; those pieces of skulls lying around filled with earth, in which a flower springs up sometimes and grows through the holes of the eyes; even the vulgarity of those inscriptions, which are as similar as the corpses they identify — all this human rottenness appeared beautiful to us, and procured us a splendid sight.

If the post of Auray had arrived, we should have started at once for Belle-Isle; but they were waiting for it. Transient sailors with bare arms and open shirts sat in the kitchen of the inn, drinking to pass away the time.

"At what time is the post due here in Auray?"

"That depends; usually at ten o'clock," replied the innkeeper.

"No, at eleven," put in a man.

"At twelve," said M. de Rohan.

"At one."

"At half-past one."

"Sometimes it doesn't reach here until two o'clock."

"It isn't very regular!"

We were aware of that; it was already three. We could not start before the arrival of this ill-fated messenger, which brings Belle-Isle the despatches from *terra firma,* so we had to resign ourselves. Once in a while some one would get up, go to the door, look out, come back, and start up again. Oh! he will not come to-day. — He must have stopped on the way. — Let's go home. — No, let's wait for him. — If, however, you are tired of waiting gentlemen. . . . After all, there may not be any letters. . . . No, just wait a little longer. — Oh! here he comes! — But it was some one else, and the dialogue would begin all over again.

At last we heard the beating of tired hoofs on the cobblestones, the tinkling of bells, the cracking of a whip and a man's voice shouting: "Ho! Ho! Here's the post! Here's the post!"

The horse stopped in front of the door, hunched its back, stretched its neck, opened its mouth, disclosed its teeth, spread its hind legs and rose on its hocks.

The animal was lean and tall, and had a moth-eaten mane, rough hoofs and loose shoes; a seton bobbed up and down on its breast. Lost in a saddle that swallowed him up, supported at the back by a valise and in front by the mail-bag, which was passed through the saddle-bow, its rider sat huddled on it like a monkey. His small face, adorned with straggling blond whiskers and as wrinkled and rough as a winter apple, was hidden by a large oil-cloth hat lined with felt; a sort of gray coutil coat was drawn up to his hips and bagged around his stomach, while his trousers stopped at the knees and disclosed his bare legs reddened by the rubbing of the stirrup-straps, and his blue hose, which hung over his shoes. The harness was held together with strings, the rider's clothes had been mended with threads of different colours; all sorts of patches and all kinds of spots, torn linen, greasy leather, dried mud, recent dust, hanging straps, bright rags, a dirty man and a mangy horse, the ıormer sickly and perspiring, the latter consumptive and almost spent; the one with his whip and the other with its bells — all this formed but one object which had the same colour and movement and executed almost the same gestures, which served the same purpose, the conducting of the Auray post.

After another hour, when all the packages and commissions had been attended to and we had waited for several passengers who were to come, we finally left the inn and went aboard. At first there was nothing but a confused mass of people and luggage, oars that caused us to stumble, sails that dropped on our heads, men falling over each other and not knowing where to go; then everything quieted down, each one found his nook, the luggage was put in the bottom of the boat, the sailors got on the benches, and the passengers seated themselves as best they could.

There was no breeze and the sails clung limply to the masts. The heavy boat hardly moved over the almost motionless sea, which swelled and subsided with the gentle rhythm of a sleeping breast.

Leaning against one of the gunwales, we gazed at the water, which was as blue and calm as the sky, and listened to the splashing of the oars; sitting in the shadow of the sail, the six rowers lifted their oars regularly to make the forward stroke, and when they dipped them into the water and brought them up again, drops of crystal clung to their paddles. Reclining on the straw, or sitting on the benches, with their legs dangling and their chins in their hands, or leaning against the sides of the boat, between the big jambs of the hull, the tar of which was melting in the heat, the silent passengers hung their heads and closed their eyes to shut out the glare of the sun, that shone on the flat ocean as on a mirror.

A white-haired man was sleeping at my feet, a gendarme was sweltering under his three-cornered hat, and two soldiers had unfastened their knapsacks and used them as pillows. Near the bowsprit stood a cabin-boy looking into the stay-sail and whistling for wind, while the skipper remained aft and managed the tiller. Still no wind arose. Orders were given to haul in the sails; slowly and gently they came down and fell in a heap on the benches; then each sailor took off his waistcoat, stowed it away under the bow of the boat, and the men began to row again with all their might.

Our departure had been so delayed that there was hardly any water left in the harbour and we had great difficulty in landing. Our boat grated on the pebbles, and in order to leave it, we were compelled to walk on an oar as if it were a tight-rope.

Ensconced between the citadel and its ramparts, and cut in two by an almost empty port, the Palay appeared to us a useless little town overcome with military ennui, and put me in mind, I do not know why, of a gaping *sous-officier*.

One fails to see the low-crowned, broad-brimmed black felt hats of Le Morbihan, that give protection to the shoulders as well as the head. The women do not affect the big, white caps that stand out from their faces, and reach down their backs like those worn by the nuns, so that when worn by little girls they cover half of their bodies. Their gowns are made without the wide stripe of velvet applied on each shoulder and rounding away under the arms. Nor do they wear the low shoes with square toes, high heels, and long black ribbon streamers. Here, as elsewhere, we found faces that resemble other faces, costumes that really are no costumes at all, cobblestones, and even a sidewalk.

Was it worth while to expose ourselves to sea-sickness (which, by the way, we escaped, a fact that inclined us to leniency), only to see a citadel that we do not admire, a lighthouse that did not appeal to us in the least, and a rampart built by Vauban, of whom we were already heartily tired? But people had spoken to us of Belle-Isle's rocks. So we started at once, and taking a short cut across the fields, walked to the beach.

We saw one grotto, only one (the day was near its close), but it appeared so beautiful to us (it was draped with sea-weed and decorated with shells, and water dripped from the top), that we resolved to spend a day in Belle-Isle, in order to discover more of them, if there were any, and feast our eyes leisurely upon their beauties.

The following day, at dawn, having filled our flasks and put some sandwiches in our knapsacks, we decided to go where we pleased; so, without a guide or information of any sort (this is the best way), we set out to walk, having resolved that we would go anywhere, provided it were far, and would return home at any time, provided it were late.

We began by a path which led to the top of a cliff, then followed its asperities and valleys and continued around the whole island. When we reached places where landslips had obliterated it, we struck out into the country and let our eyes roam over the horizon of the sea, the deep blue line of which touched the sky; then we walked back to the edge of the rocks, whcih had suddenly reappeared at our side. The perpendicular cliff, the top of which we were treading, concealed the flank of the rocks, and we could only hear the roaring of the breakers below us.

Sometimes the rock was split in its entire length, disclosing its two almost straight sides, streaked with layers of silica, with tufts of yellow flowers scattered here and there. If we threw a stone, it appeared suspended in the air for a time, would then strike the sides of the cliff, rebound from the one to the other, break into a thousand bits, scattering earth and pebbles in its course, and finally land at the bottom of the pit, where it frightened the cormorants, which shrieked and took flight.

Frequent storms and thaws have pushed a part of the upper grounds into these gorges, and so their steep slope has grown less abrupt, and one is able to climb down to the bottom. We attempted to do so by sliding down like children, holding ourselves back with our hands and feet, and finally we landed safely on the soft, wet sand.

The tide was going out, but in order to be able to pass, we had to wait until the breakers receded. We watched them approach us. They dashed against the rocks, swirled in the crevices, rose like scarfs on the wind, fell back in drops and sprays, and with one long, sweeping libration, gathered their green waters together and retreated. When one wave left the sand, its currents immediately joined, and sought lower levels. The sea-weed moved its slimy branches; the water bubbled between the pebbles, oozed through the cracks of the rocks and formed a thousand rivulets and fountains. The drenched sand absorbed it all, and soon its yellow tint grew white again through the drying action of the sun.

As soon as we could, we jumped over the rocks and continued on our way. Soon, however, they increased in numbers, their weird groups being crowded together, piled up and overturned on one another. We tried to hold on with our hands and feet, but we slid on their slippery asperities. The cliff was so very high that it quite frightened us to look up at it. Although it crushed us by its formidable placidity, still it fascinated us, for we could not help looking at it and it did not tire our eyes.

A swallow passed us and we watched its flight; it came from the sea; it ascended slowly through the air, cutting the luminous, fluid atmosphere with its sharp, outstretched wings that seemed to enjoy being absolutely untrammelled. The bird ascended higher and higher, rose above the cliff and finally disappeared.

Meanwhile we were creeping over the rocks, the perspective of which was renewed by each bend of the coast. Once in a while, when the rocks ended, we walked on square stones that were as flat as marble slabs and seamed by almost symmetrical furrows, which appeared like the tracks of some ancient road of another world.

In some places were great pools of water as calm as their greenish depths and as limpid and motionless as a woodland stream on its bed of cresses. Then the rocks would reappear closer than before and more numerous. On one side was the ocean with its breakers foaming around the lower rocks; on the other, the straight, unrelenting, impassive coast.

Tired and bewildered, we looked about us for some issue; but the cliff stretched out before us, and the rocks, infinitely multiplying their dark green forms, succeeded one another until their unequal crags seemed like so many tall, black phantoms rising out of the earth.

We stumbled around in this way until we suddenly perceived an undulating series of rough steps which enabled us to climb up to flat land again.

It is always a pleasure, even when the country is ugly, to walk with a friend, to feel the grass under one's feet, to jump over fences and ditches, to break thistles with one's stick, to pull leaves from the bushes and wheat from the fields, to go where one's fancy dictates, whistling, singing, talking, dreaming, without strange ears to listen to one's conversation, and the sound of strange footsteps behind one, as absolutely free as if one were in the desert!

Ah! Let us have air! air! And more space! Since our contracted souls suffocate and die on the window-sill, since our captive spirits, like the bear in its cage, turn around and around, and stagger against the walls of their prison, why not, at least, let our nostrils breathe the different perfumes of all the winds of the earth, why not let our eyes rove over every horizon?

No steeple shone in the distance, no hamlet with thatched roofs and square yards framed by clusters of trees, appeared on the side of a hill; not a soul was to be seen, not even a peasant, a grazing sheep, or a stray dog.

All those cultivated fields look uninhabited; the peasants work in them, but they do not live there. One is led to believe that they benefit by them but do not care about them in the least.

We saw a farm and walked in; a ragged woman served us some ice-cold milk in earthen cups. The silence all around was peculiar. The woman watched us eagerly, and we soon took our departure.

We walked into a valley, the narrow gorge of which appeared to extend to the ocean. Tall grass with yellow flowers reached up to our waists, and we had to take long strides in order to advance.

We could hear the murmur of flowing water near by, and we sank ankle-deep into the marshy soil. Presently the two hills parted; their barren sides were covered with short, stubby grass and here and there were big yellow patches of moss. At the foot of one hill a stream wends its way through the drooping boughs of the stunted shrubs that grow on its edges, and loses itself in a quiet pond where long-legged insects disport themselves on the leaves of the water-lilies. The sun beat down on us. The gnats rubbed their wings together and bent the slender ends of the reeds with the weight of their tiny bodies. We were alone in the tranquillity of this desert.

At this point, the valley curved and widened and formed a sharp bend. We climbed a little hill, in order to locate ourselves, but the horizon either ended abruptly, enclosed by another hill, or else stretched out over new plains. We did not lose courage, however, and continued to advance, while we thought of the travellers on desert islands who climb on promontories in the hope of sighting some vessel setting sail towards them.

The soil was growing less moist, and the grass less high; presently the ocean came in view, ensconced in a narrow bay, and soon the shore, strewn with débris of shells and madrepores, crunched beneath our footsteps. We let ourselves drop to the ground and as we were exhausted, we soon fell asleep. An hour later the cold woke us up, and we started homeward without any fear of losing our way this time. We were on the coast facing France, and Palay was on our left. It was here, the day before, that we had discovered the grotto we admired so much. It did not take us long to find others, higher and deeper even than the first one.

They always opened through large, pointed arches which were either upright or inclined, their bold columns supporting enormous pieces of rock. Black, veined with purple, fiery red, or brown streaked with white, these beautiful grottoes displayed for their visitors the infinite variety of their shapes and colouring, their graces and their grand caprices. There was one all of silver veined with deep red; in another, tufts of flowers resembling periwinkles had grown on glazings of reddish granite, and drops of water fell from the ceiling on the fine sand with never-ceasing regularity. In the background of another grotto, beneath a long semi-circle, a bed of polished white gravel, which the tide no doubt turns and makes fresh every day, seemed to be waiting to receive the body of a mermaid; but the bed is empty and has lost her forever! Only the moist seaweed remains on which she used to stretch her delicate nude limbs when she was tired of swimming, and on which she reclined till daybreak, in the pale light of the moon.

The sun was setting, and the tide was coming in over the rocks that melted in the blue evening mist, which was blanched on the level of the ocean by the foam of the tumbling waves. In the other part of the horizon, the sky streaked with orange stripes looked as if it had been swept by a gale. Its light reflected on the waters and spread a gleaming sheen over them, and projected on the sand, giving it a brownish tinge and making it glitter like steel.

Half a mile to the south, the coast is covered by a line of rocks that extends to the sea. In order to reach them, we should have been compelled to tramp as we had already done that morning. We were tired, and it was far; but a temptation seemed to push us forward. The breeze played in the cracks of the rocks and wrinkled the surface of the pools; the sea-weed, cleaving to the sides of the cliff, shook in the wind, and from the part of the sky where the moon was to rise, a pale light spread over the waters. It was the hour when the shadows lengthen. The rocks appeared larger, and the breakers a deeper green. The sky seemed to expand, and all nature assumed a different appearance.

So we started, without giving a thought to the incoming tide or whether or not we should find later a way to get back to land. We wished to enjoy our pleasure to the fullest extent. We seemed lighter than in the morning, and ran and jumped without the slightest feeling of fatigue. An abundance of animal spirits impelled us onward and we felt a peculiarly robust twitching in our muscles. We shook our heads in the wind and touched the grasses with our fingers. We breathed the salt air of the ocean, and noted and assimilated every color, every sunbeam, every sound, the design of the seaweed, the softness of the sand, the hardness of the rocks that echoed under our footsteps, the height of the cliffs, the fringe of the waves, the accidents of the coast, and the voice of the horizon; and the breeze that passed over our faces like intangible kisses, the sky with its passing clouds, the rising moon, the peeping stars. Our souls bathed in all this splendour, and our eyes feasted on it; we opened our ears and nostrils wide; something of the very life of the elements, forced from them undoubtedly by the attraction of our eyes, reached us and was assimilated, so that we were able to comprehend them in a closer relation and feel them more keenly, thanks to this complex union.

By thus entering and penetrating into nature, we became a part of it, diffused ourselves in it, and were claimed by it once more; we felt that it was overpowering us, and we rejoiced; we desired to be lost in it, to be borne away, or to carry it away with us. As in the raptures of love, one wishes more hands with which to caress, more lips with which to kiss, more eyes with which to see, more soul with which to worship; spreading ourselves out in nature, with a joyful and delirious abandon, we regretted that our eyes could not penetrate to the innermost parts of the rocks, to the bottom of the sea, to the end of the heavens, in order to see how the stones grow, how the breakers are made, how the stars are lighted; we regretted that our ears could not catch the rumour of the fermentation of the granite in the bowels of the earth, could not hear the sap circulate in the plants and the coral roll in the solitudes of the ocean. And while we were under the spell of that contemplative effusion, we wished that our souls, radiating everywhere, might live all these different lives, assume all these different forms, and, varying unceasingly, accomplish their metamorphoses under an eternal sun!

But man was made to enjoy each day only a small portion of food, colours, sounds, sentiments and ideas. Anything above the allotted quantity tires or intoxicates him; it becomes the idiocy of the drunkard or the ravings of the ecstatic. O, God! How small is our glass and how large is our thirst! What weak heads we have!

CHAPTER V.

RETURN.

IN ORDER to return to Quiberon, we were compelled, on the following day, to arise before seven o'clock, a feat which required some courage. While we were still stiff from fatigue and shivering with sleep, we got into a boat along with a white horse, two drummers, the same one-eyed gendarme and the same soldier who, this time, however, did not lecture anybody. As drunk as a lord, he kept slipping under the benches and had all he could do to keep his shako on his head and extricate his gun from between his feet. I could not say which was the sillier of the two. The gendarme was sober, but he was very stupid. He deplored the soldier's lack of manners, enumerated the punishments that would be dealt out to him, was 'scandalised by his hiccoughs and resented his demeanour. Viewed from the side of the missing eye, with his three-cornered hat, his sabre and his yellow gloves, the gendarme presented one of the sorriest aspects of human life. Besides, there is something so essentially grotesque about gendarmes that I cannot help laughing at them; these

(50)

upholders of the law always produce the same comic effect on me, and so do attorneys for the king, magistrates, and professors of literature.

Tipped to one side, the boat skimmed lightly through the foaming waves. The three sails were comfortably swelled; the masts creaked and the wind rattled the pulleys. A cabin-boy stood at the helm singing. We could not catch the words, but it was some slow, monotonous lay which neither rose nor fell and was repeated again and again, with long-drawn-out inflections and languid refrain. And it swept softly and sadly out over the ocean, as some confused memory sweeps through one's mind.

The horse stood as straight as it could on its four legs and pulled at a bundle of hay. The sailors, with folded arms, looked absently at the sails and smiled a far-away smile.

So we journeyed on without speaking a word and as best we could, without reaching the edge of the bay, where it looked as if Plonharnel might be. However, after a while we arrived there. But when we did, we were confronted by the ocean, for we had followed the right side of the coast instead of the left, and were forced to turn back and go over a part of the route.

A muffled sound was heard. A bell tinkled and a hat appeared. It was the Auray post. Again the same man, the same horse, the same mail-bag. He was ambling quietly towards Quiberon; he would be back directly and return again the next day. He is the guest of the coast; he passes in the morning and again at night. His life is spent going from one point to another; he is the only one who gives the coast some animation, something to look forward to, and, I was almost going to say, some charm.

He stopped and talked to us for a few minutes, then lifted his hat and was off again.

What an ensemble! What a horse, and what a rider! What a picture! Callot would probably have reproduced it, but it would take Cervantes to write it.

After passing over large pieces of rock that have been placed in the sea in order to shorten the route by cutting the back of the bay in two, we finally arrived at Plouharnel.

The village was quiet; chickens cackled and scratched in the streets, and in the gardens enclosed by stone walls, weeds and oats grew side by side.

While we were sitting in front of the host's door, an old beggar passed us. He was as red as a lobster, dirty and unkempt and covered with rags and vermin. The sun shone on his dilapidated garments and on his purple skin; it was almost black and seemed to transude blood. He kept bellowing in a terrible voice, while beating a tattoo on the door of a neighbouring house.

CHAPTER VI.

QUIMPER.

QUIMPER, although it is the centre of the real Brittany, is distinctly different from it. The elm-tree promenade that follows the winding river, which has quays and boats, renders the town very pretty and the big Hôtel de la Préfecture, which alone covers the little western delta, gives it a thoroughly administrative and French appearance. You are aware that you are in the *chef-lieu* of a department, a fact brought home to you by the latter's division in *arrondissements,* with their large, medium, and small parishes, its committee of primary instruction, its saving banks, its town council and other modern inventions, which rob the cities of local colour, dear to the heart of the innocent tourist.

With all due deference to the people who pronounce the name of Quimper-Corentin as the synonyme of all that is ridiculous and provincial, it is a most delightful place, and well worth other more respected ones. You will not, it is true, find the charms and riotous wealth of colouring possessed by Quimperlé; still, I know of few things that can equal the charming appearance of that alley following the edge of the river and shaded by the escarpment of a neighbouring mountain, which casts the dark shadows of its luxuriant foliage over it.

It does not take long to go through cities of this kind, and to know their most intimate recesses, and sometimes one stumbles across places that stay one's steps and fill one's heart with gladness.

Small cities, like small apartments, seem warmer and cosier to live in. But keep this illusion! There are more draughts in such apartments than in a palace, and a city of this kind is more deadly monotonous than the desert.

Returning to the hotel by one of those paths we dearly love, that rises and falls and winds, sometimes through a field, sometimes through grass and brambles, sometimes along a wall, which are filled in turn with daisies, pebbles and thistles, a path made for light thoughts and bantering conversation,—returning, I said, to the city, we heard cries and plaintive wails issue from under the slated roof of a square building. It was the slaughter-house.

At that moment I thought of some terrible city, of some frightful and immense place like Babylon or Babel, filled with cannibals and slaughter-houses where they butchered men instead of animals; and I tried to discover a likeness to human agonies in those bleating and sobbing voices. I thought of groups of slaves brought there with ropes around their necks, to be tied to iron rings, and killed in order to feed their masters, who would eat their flesh from tables of carved ivory and wipe their lips on fine linen. Would their attitudes be more dejected, their eyes sadder or their prayers more pitiful?

While we were in Quimper, we went out one day through one side of the town and came back through the other, after tramping about eight hours.

Our guide was waiting for us under the porch of the hotel. He started in front of us and we followed. He was a little white-haired man, with a linen cap and torn shoes, and he wore an old brown coat that was many sizes too large for him. He stuttered when he spoke, and when he walked he knocked his knees together; but in spite of all this, he managed to advance very quickly, with a sort of nervous, almost febrile perseverance. From time to time, he would pull a leaf off a tree and clap it over his mouth to cool his lips. His business consists in going from one place to another, attending to letters and errands. He goes to Douarnenez, Quimperlé, Brest and even to Rennes, which is forty miles away (a journey which he accomplished in four days, including going and coming). His whole ambition, he said, was to return to Rennes once more during his lifetime. And only for the purpose, mind you, of going back, of making the trip, and being able to boast of it afterwards. He knows every road and every *commune* that has a steeple; he takes short cuts across the fields, opens gates, and when he passes in front of a farm, he never fails to greet its owners. Having listened to the birds all his life, he has learned to imitate their chirpings, and when he walks along the roads, under the trees, he whistles as his feathered friends do, in order to charm his solitude.

Our first stop was at Loc-Maria, an ancient monastery, given in olden times by Conan III to the abbey of Fontevrault; it is situated a quarter of a mile from the town. This monastery has not been shame-

fully utilised like the abbey of poor Robert d'Arbris-
sel.* It is deserted, but has not been sullied. Its
Gothic portal does not re-echo the voices of jailers,
and though there may not be much of it, one experiences neither disgust nor rebellion. In that little
chapel, of a rather severe Romance style, the only
curious thing is a large granite holy-water basin
which stands on the floor and is almost black. It is
wide and deep and represents to perfection the real
Catholic holy-water basin, made to receive the entire
body of an infant, and not in the least like those
narrow shells in our churches in which you can only
dip your fingers. With its clear water rendered more
limpid by the contrast of a greenish bed, the vegeta-
tion which has grown all around it during the religious calm of centuries, its crumbling angles, and
its great mass of bronzed stone, it looks like one of
those hollowed rocks which contain salt water.

After we had inspected the chapel carefully, we
walked to the river, crossed it in a boat, and plunged
into the country.

It is absolutely deserted and strangely empty.
Trees, bushes, sea-rushes, tamarisks, and heather grow
on the edge of the ditches. We came to broad
stretches of land, but we did not see a soul anywhere.
The sky was bleak and a fine rain moistened the atmosphere and spread a grey veil over the country.
The paths we chose were hollow and shaded by
clusters of foliage, the branches of which, uniting,
drooped over our heads and almost prevented us
from walking erect. The light that filtered through
the dome of leaves was greenish, and as dim as on a

* Founder of the abbey of Fontevrault, in 1099.

winter evening. But farther away, it was brilliant, and played around the edges of the leaves and accentuated their delicate pinking. Later we reached the top of a barren slope, which was flat and smooth, and without a blade of grass to relieve the monotony of its colour. Sometimes, however, we came upon a long avenue of beech-trees with moss growing around the foot of their thick, shining trunks. There were wagon-tracks in these avenues, as if to indicate the presence of a neighbouring castle that we might see at any moment; but they ended abruptly in a stretch of flat land that continued between two valleys, through which it would spread its green maze furrowed by the capricious meanderings of hedges, spotted here and there by a grove, brightened by clumps of sea-rushes, or by some field bordering the meadows which rose slowly to meet the hills and lost themselves in the horizon. Above these hills, far away in the mist, stretched the blue surface of the ocean.

The birds are either absent or they do not sing; the leaves are thick, the grass deadens one's foot-falls, and the country gazes at you like some melancholy countenance. It looks as if it had been created expressly to harbour ruined lives and shattered hopes, and to foster their bitterness beneath its weeping sky, to the low rustling of the trees and the heather. On winter nights, when the fox creeps stealthily over the dry leaves, when the tiles fall from the pigeon-house and the reeds bend in the marshes, when the beech-trees stoop in the wind, and the wolf ambles over the moonlit snow, while one is alone by the dying embers listening to the wind howl in the empty hallways, how charming it must be to let one's heart dwell on its most cherished despairs and long forgotten loves!

We spied a hovel with a Gothic portal; further on was an old wall with an ogive door; a leafless bush swayed there in the breeze. In the courtyard the ground is covered with heather, violets, and pebbles; you walk in, look around and go out again. This place is called "The temple of the false gods," and used to be, it is thought, a commandery of Templars.

Our guide started again and we followed him. Presently a steeple rose among the trees; we crossed a stubble-field, climbed to the top of a ditch and caught a glimpse of a few of dwellings: the village of Pomelin. A rough road constitutes the main street and the village consists of several houses separated by yards. What tranquillity! or rather what forlornness! The thresholds are deserted; the yards are empty.

Where are the inhabitants? One would think that they had all left the village to lie in wait behind the furze-bushes to catch a glimpse of the *Blues* who are about to pass through the ravine.

The church is poor and perfectly bare. No beautiful painted saints, no pictures on the walls or on the roof, no hanging lamp oscillating at the end of a long, straight cord. In a corner of the choir, a wick was burning in a glass filled with oil. Round wooden pillars hold up the roof, the blue paint of which has been freshened recently. The bright light of the fields, filtering through the green foliage which covers the roof of the church, shines through the white window-panes. The door, a little wooden door that closes with a latch, was open; a flight of birds came in, chirping and beating their wings against the walls; they fluttered for awhile beneath the vault and around the altar, two or three alighted upon the holy-water basin, to moisten their beaks, and then all flew away as suddenly as they had come.

It is not an unusual thing to see birds in the Breton churches; many live there and fasten their nests to the stones of the nave; they are never disturbed. When it rains, they all gather in the church, but as soon as the sun pierces the clouds and the rain-spouts dry up, they repair to the trees again. So that during the storm two frail creatures often enter the blessed house of God together; man to pray and allay his fears, and the bird to wait until the rain stops and to warm the naked bodies of its frightened young.

A peculiar charm pervades these churches. It is not their poverty that moves us, because even when they are empty, they appear to be inhabited. Is it not, then, their modesty that appeals to us? For, with their unpretentious steeples, and their low roofs hiding under the trees, they seem to shrink and humiliate themselves in the sight of God. They have not been upreared through a spirit of pride, nor through the pious fancy of some mighty man on his death-bed. On the contrary, we feel that it is the simple impression of a need, the ingenuous cry of an appetite, and, like the shepherd's bed of dried leaves, it is the retreat the soul has built for itself where it comes to rest when it is tired. These village churches represent better than their city sisters the distinctive features of the places where they are built, and they seem to participate more directly in the life of the people who, from father to son, come to kneel at the same place and on the same stone slab. Every day, every Sunday, when they enter and when they leave, do they not see the graves of their parents, are these not near them while they pray, and does it not seem to them as if the church was only a larger family circle from which the loved ones have not altogether departed? These places of worship thus have a harmonious sense, and the life of these people is influenced by it from the baptismal font to the grave. It is not the same with us, because we have relegated eternity to the outskirts of the city, have banished our dead to the faubourgs and laid them to rest in the carpenter's quarter, near the soda factories and night-soil magazines.

About three o'clock in the afternoon, we arrived at the chapel of Kerfeunteun, near the entrance to Quimper. At the upper end of the chapel is a fine glass window of the sixteenth century, representing the genealogical tree of the Holy Trinity. Jacob forms the trunk, and the top is figured by the Cross surmounted by the Eternal Father with a tiara on His head. On each side, the square steeple represents a quadrilateral pierced by a long straight window. This steeple does not rest squarely on the roof, but instead, by means of a slender basis, the narrow sides of which almost touch, it forms an obtuse angle near the ridge of the roof. In Brittany, almost every church has a steeple of this kind.

Before returning to the city, we made a détour in order to visit the chapel of *La Mère-Dieu*. As it is usually closed, our guide summoned the custodian, and the latter accompanied us with his little niece, who stopped along the road to pick flowers. The young man walked in front of us. His slender and flexible figure was encased in a jacket of light blue cloth, and the three velvet streamers of his black hat, which was carefully placed on the back of his head, over his knotted hair, hung down his back.

At the bottom of a valley, or rather a ravine, can be seen the church of *La Mère-Dieu*, veiled by thick foliage. In this place, amid the silence of all these trees and because of its little Gothic portal (which appears to be of the thirteenth century, but which, in reality, is of the sixteenth), the church reminds one of the discreet chapels mentioned in old novels and old melodies, where they knighted the page starting for the Holy Land, one morning when the stars were dim and the lark trilled, while the mistress of the castle slipped her white hand through the bars of the iron gate and wept when he kissed her good-bye.

We entered the church. The young custodian took off his hat and knelt on the floor. His thick, blond hair uncoiled and fell around his shoulders. It clung a moment to the coarse cloth of his jacket, and then, little by little, it separated and spread like the hair of a woman. It was parted in the middle and hung on both sides over his shoulders and neck. The golden mass rippled with light every time he moved his head bent in prayer.

The little girl kneeled beside him and let her flowers fall to the ground. For the first time in my life, I understood the beauty of a man's locks and the fascination they may have for bare and playful arms. A strange progress, indeed, is that which consists in curtailing everywhere the grand superfetations nature has bestowed upon us, so that whenever we discover them in all their virgin splendour, they are a revelation to us.

CHAPTER VII.

PONT-L'ABBÉ.

AT FIVE o'clock in the evening, we arrived at Pont-l'Abbé, covered with quite a respectable coating of mud and dust, which fell from our clothing upon the floor of the inn with such disastrous abundance, every time we moved, that we were almost mortified at the mess we made.

Pont-l'Abbé is a peaceful little town, cut in two in its entire length by a broad, paved street. Its modest inhabitants cannot possibly look any more stupid or insignificant than the place itself.

For those who must see something wherever they go, there are the unimportant remains of the castle and the church, an edifice that would be quite passable were it not for the thick coat of paint that covers it. The chapel of the Virgin was a bower of flowers; bunches of jonquils, pansies, roses, jessamine, and honeysuckle were arranged in blue glasses or white china vases and spread their bright colours over the altar and upward between the two tall candlesticks framing the Virgin's face and her silver crown, from which fell a long veil caught on the gold star

of the plaster Infant she held in her arms. One could
smell the odour of the holy water and the flowers. It
was a perfumed, mysterious little nook all by itself,
a hidden retreat decorated by loving hands, and peculiarly adapted for the exhalation of mystical desires and
long, heart-broken orisons. All his heart's sensuous-
ness, compressed by the climate and numbed by misery,
is brought here by man and laid at the feet of Mary,
the Divine Mother, and he is thus able to satisfy his
unquenchable longing for love and enjoyment. No
matter if the roof leaks and there are no benches or
chairs in the rest of the church, you will always find
the chapel of the Virgin bright with flowers and
lights, for it seems as if all the religious tenderness
of Brittany has concentrated there; it is the softest
spot of its heart; it is its weakness, its passion,
its treasure. Though there are no flowers in these
parts, there are flowers in the church; though the
people are poor, the Virgin is always sumptuous
and beautiful. She smiles at you, and despairing souls
go to warm themselves at her knees as at a hearth-
stone that is never extinguished. One is astonished
at the way these people cling to their belief; but
does one know the pleasure and voluptuousness they
derive from it? Is not asceticism superior epicu-
reanism, fasting, refined gormandising? Religion can
supply one with almost carnal sensations; prayer has
its debauchery and mortification its raptures; and the
men who come at night and kneel in front of this
dressed statue, feel their hearts beat thickly and a sort
of vague intoxication, while in the streets of the
city, the children on their way home from school
stop and gaze dreamily at the woman who smiles at
them from the stained window of the church.

But you must attend a fête in order to gain an insight into the gloomy character of these people. They don't dance; they merely turn; they don't sing; they only whistle. That very evening we went to a neighbouring village to be present at the inauguration of a threshing-floor. Two *biniou* players were stationed on top of the wall surrounding the yard, and played continuously while two long lines of men and women, following in one anothers' footsteps, trotted around the place and described several figures. The lines would turn, break up and form again at irregular intervals. The heavy feet of the dancers struck the ground without the slightest attempt at rhythm, while the shrill notes of the music succeeded one another rapidly and with desperate monotony. The dancers who tired withdrew without interrupting the dance, and when they had rested, they re-entered it. During the whole time we watched this peculiar performance, the crowd stopped only once, while the musicians drank some cider; then, when they had finished, the lines formed anew and the dance began again. At the entrance of the yard was a table covered with nuts; beside it stood a pitcher of brandy and on the ground was a keg of cider; near by stood a citizen in a green frock coat and a leather cap; a little farther away was a man wearing a jacket and a sword suspended from a white shoulder-belt; they were the *commissaire de police,* of Pont-l'Abbé and his *garde-champêtre.* Suddenly, M. le commissaire pulled out his watch and motioned to the *garde.* The latter drew several peasants aside, spoke to them in a low tone, and presently the assembly broke up.

All four of us returned to the city together, which afforded us the opportunity of again admiring another of the harmonious combinations of Providence which had created this *commissaire de police* for this *garde-champêtre* and this *garde-champêtre* for this *commissaire de police*. They were made for each other. The same fact would give rise in both of them to the same reflections; from the same idea both would draw parallel conclusions. When the *commissaire* laughed, the *garde* grinned; when he assumed a serious expression, his shadow grew gloomy; if the frock-coat said, "This must be done," the jacket replied, "I think so, too;" if the coat added, "It is necessary;" the waistcoat affirmed: "It is indispensable." Notwithstanding this inward comprehension, their outward relations of rank and authority remained unchanged. For the *garde* spoke in a lower tone than the *commissaire,* and was a trifle shorter and walked behind him. The *commissaire* was polished, important, fluent; he consulted himself, ruminated, talked to himself, and smacked his tongue; the *garde* was deferential, attentive, pensive and observing, and would utter an exclamation from time to time and scratch his nose. On the way, he inquired about the news, asked the *commissaire's* advice, and solicited his orders, while his superior questioned, meditated, and issued commands.

We had just come in sight of the first houses of the city, when we heard shrieks issue from one of them. The street was blocked by an excited crowd, and several persons rushed up to the *commissaire* and exclaimed: "Come, come quickly, Monsieur, they're having a fight! Two women are being killed!"

"By whom?"

"We don't know."

"Why?"

7—16

"They are bleeding."

"But with what?"

"With a rake."

"Where's the murderer?"

"One on the head and the other on the arm. Go in, they're waiting for you; the women are there."

So the *commissaire* went in and we followed. We heard sobs, screams, and excited conversation and saw a jostling, curious mob. People stepped on one another's toes, dug one another's ribs, cursed, and caused general confusion.

The *commissaire* got angry; but as he could not speak Breton, the *garde* got angry for him and chased the crowd out, taking each individual by his shoulders and shoving him through the door into the street.

When the room had been cleared of all except a dozen persons, we managed to discover in a corner, a piece of flesh hanging from an arm and a mass of black hair dripping with blood. An old woman and a young girl had been hurt in the fight. The old woman was tall and angular and had skin as yellow and wrinkled as parchment; she was standing up, groaning and holding her left arm with her right hand; she did not seem to be suffering much, but the girl was crying. She was sitting on a chair with her hands spread out on her knees and her head bent low; she was trembling convulsively and shaking with low sobs. As they replied by complaints to all our questions, and as the testimony of the witnesses was conflicting, we could not ascertain who had started the fight or what it was about. Some said that a husband had surprised his wife; others, that the women had started the row and that the owner of the house had tried to kill them in order to make them stop. But no one knew anything definite. M. *le commissaire* was greatly perplexed and the *garde* perfectly nonplussed.

As the doctor was away, and as it might be that the good people did not wish his services, because it meant expense, we had the audacity to offer the help of our limited knowledge and rushed off for our satchels, a piece of cerecloth, and some linen and lint which we had brought with us in anticipation of possible accidents.

It would really have been an amusing sight for our friends, had they been able to see us spread out our bistoury, our pincers, and three pairs of scissors, one with gold branches, on the table of this hut. The *commissaire* praised our philanthropy, the women watched us in awed silence, and the tallow candle melted and ran down the iron candle-stick in spite of the efforts of the *garde,* who kept trimming the wick with his fingers. We attended to the old woman first. The cut had been given conscientiously; the bare arm showed the bone, and a triangle of flesh about four inches long hung over it like a cuff. We tried to put this back in its place by adjusting it carefully over the edge of the gaping wound and bandaging the arm. It is quite possible that the violent compression the member was subjected to caused mortification to set in, and that the patient may have died.

We did not know exactly what ailed the girl. The blood trickled through her hair, but we could not see whence it came; it formed oily blotches all over it and ran down into her neck. The *garde,* our interpreter, bade her remove the cotton band she

wore on her head, and her tresses tumbled down in
a dull, dark mass and uncoiled like a cascade full of
bloody threads. We parted the thick, soft, abundant
locks, and found a swelling as large as a nut and
pierced by an oval hole on the back of her head.
We shaved the surrounding parts; and after we had
washed and stanched the wound, we melted some
tallow and spread it over some lint, which we adapted
to the swelling with strips of diachylum. Over this
we placed first a bandage, then the cotton band, and
then the cap. While this was taking place, the
justice of the peace arrived. The first thing he did
was to ask for the rake, and the only thing he seemed
to care about was to examine it. He took hold of
the handle, counted the teeth, waved it in the air,
tested the iron and bent the wood.

"Is this," he demanded, "the instrument with
which the assault was committed? Jérôme, are you
sure it is?"

"They say so, Monsieur."

"You were not present, Monsieur le commissaire?"

"No, Monsieur le juge de paix."

"I would like to know whether the blows were
really dealt with a rake or whether they were given
with a blunt instrument. Who is the assailant? And
did the rake belong to him or to some one else?
Was it really with this that these women were hurt?
Or was it, I repeat, with a blunt instrument? Do
they wish to lodge a complaint? What do you think
about it, Monsieur le commissaire?"

The victims said little, remarking only that they
suffered great pain; so they were given over night to
decide whether or not they wished to seek redress by
law. The young girl could hardly speak, and the

old woman's ideas were muddled, seeing that she was drunk, according to what the neighbours intimated,—a fact which explained her insensibility when we had endeavoured to relieve her suffering.

After they had looked at us as keenly as they could in order to ascertain who we were, the authorities of Pont-l'Abbé bade us good night and thanked us for the services we had rendered the community. We put our things back into our satchel, and the *commissaire* departed with the *garde,* the *garde* with his sword, and the justice of the peace with the rake.

CHAPTER VIII.

ROAMING.

E N ROUTE! the sky is blue, the sun is shining, and our feet are eager to tread on the grass. From Crozon to Leudevenec the country is quite flat, and there is not a house nor a tree to be seen. As far as the eye can reach, reddish moss spreads over the ground. Sometimes fields of ripe wheat rise above the little stunted sea-rushes. The latter are flowerless now, and look as they did before the springtime. Deep wagon-tracks, edged by rolls of dried mud, make their appearance and continue for a long time; then they suddenly describe a bend and are lost to the eye. Grass grows in large patches between these sunken furrows. The wind whistles over the flats; we walk on; a welcome breeze dries the beads of perspiration on our cheeks, and when we halted we were able to hear, above the sound of our beating arteries, the rustling of the wind in the grass.

From time to time, a mill with rapidly revolving wheels would rise up and point the way. The creaking wooden fans descended, grazed the ground and then rose. Standing erect in the open garret-window, the miller watched us pass.

We walked on; coming to a hedge of elm-trees which probably concealed a village, we caught sight of a man standing in a tree, at the foot of which was a woman with her blue apron spread out to catch the plums he was throwing to her. I recollect a crop of dark hair falling in masses over her shoulders, two uplifted arms, the movement of the supple neck and the sonorous laughter that floated over the hedge to me.

The path we were following grew narrower. Presently the plain disappeared and we found ourselves on the crest of a promontory dominating the ocean. Looking towards Brest, it seemed to extend indefinitely; but on the other side, it projected its sinuosities into the land, between short hills covered with underwood. Each gulf is ensconced between two mountains; each mountain is flanked by two gulfs, and nothing can equal the beauty of those vast green slopes rising almost in a straight line out of the sea. The hills have rounded tops and flattened bases, and describe a wide, curved chain which joins the plateaux with the graceful sweep of a Moorish arch; following so closely upon one another, the colour of their foliage and their formation are almost exactly alike. Propelled by the sea-breeze, the breakers dashed up against the foot of these hills, and the sun, falling on them, made them gleam; the whole surface of the ocean was blue and glittering with silver, and we could not get enough of its beauty. Then we watched the sunbeams glide over the hills. One of the latter had already been deserted by them, and appeared more indistinct than the rest, while a broad black shadow was rapidly gathering over another. As we approached the level of the shore the mountains that faced us a moment ago seemed to grow loftier; the gulfs deepened and the ocean expanded. We walked on, oblivious to everything, and let our eyes roam at will, and the pebbles that our feet dislodged rolled down the hill quickly and disappeared in the bushes edging the road.

The roads followed hedges that were as compact and thick as walls; we climbed up and we climbed down; meanwhile, it was growing dark, and the country was settling into the deep silence characteristic of midsummer evenings.

As we failed to meet anybody who could show us the way, the few peasants we had questioned having responded by unintelligible cries, we produced our map and our compass, and, locating ourselves by the setting sun, we resolved to head straight for Daoulas. Instantly our vigour returned, and we started across the fields, vaulting fences and ditches, and uprooting, tearing and breaking everything in our way, without giving a thought to the stiles we left open or the damaged crops.

At the top of a slope, we discovered the village of l'Hôpital lying in a meadow watered by a stream. A bridge spans the latter and on this bridge is a mill; beyond the meadow is a hill, which we started to climb nimbly, when suddenly we saw, by a ray of light, a beautiful yellow and black salamander creeping along the edge of a ditch with its slender tail dragging in the dust and undulating with every motion of its speckled body. It had come from its retreat under a big stone covered with moss, and was hunting insects in the rotten trunks of old oak-trees.

A pavement of uneven cobblestones echoed beneath our feet, and a street stretched out before us.

We had arrived in Daoulas. There was light enough to enable us to distinguish a square sign swinging on an iron rod on one of the houses. We should have recognised the inn even without the sign, as houses, like men, have their professions stamped on their faces. So we entered, for we were ravenous, and told the host above all things not to keep us waiting.

While we were sitting in front of the door, waiting for our dinner, a little girl in rags came along with a basket of strawberries on her head. She entered the inn and came out again after a short while, holding a big loaf of bread in both hands. Uttering shrill cries, she scampered off with the alertness of a kitten. Her dusty hair fluttered in the wind and stood out straight from her wizened face, and her bare legs, which she lifted high in the air when running, disappeared under the rags that covered her form.

After our meal, which comprised, besides the unavoidable omelet and the fatal veal, the strawberries the little girl had brought, we went up to our rooms.

The winding staircase with its worm-eaten steps groaned beneath our weight, like a sensitive woman under a new disillusion. At the top was a room with a door that closed on the outside with a hook. We slept there. The plaster on the once yellow walls was crumbling away; the beams of the ceiling bent beneath the weight of the slated roof, and on the window-panes was a layer of dust that softened the light like a piece of unpolished glass. The beds, four walnut boards carelessly put together, had big, round, worm-eaten knobs, and the wood was split by the dryness. On each bed was a mattress and a matting, covered with a ragged green spread. A piece of mirror in a varnished frame, an old game-bag on a nail, and a worn silk cravat which showed the crease of its folds, indicated that the room belonged to some one who probably slept there every night.

Under one of the red cotton pillows I discovered a hideous object, a cap of the same color as the coverlet, but coated with a greasy glazing which prevented its texture from being recognisable; a worn, shapeless, clammy, oily thing. I am sure that its owner prizes it highly and that he finds it warmer than any other cap. A man's life, the perspiration of an entire existence, is secreted in this layer of mouldy cerate. How many nights it must have taken to make it so thick! How many nightmares have galloped under this cap? How many dreams have been dreamed beneath it? And charming ones, too, perhaps,—why not?

If you are neither an engineer, nor a blacksmith, nor a builder, Brest will not interest you very much. The port is magnificent, I admit; beautiful, if you say so; gigantic, if you wish. It is imposing, you know, and gives the impression of a powerful nation. But those piles of cannons and anchors and cannon-balls, the infinite extension of those quays, which enclose a calm, flat sea that appears to be chained down, and those big workshops filled with grinding machinery, the never-ceasing clanking of galley chains, the convicts who pass by in regular gangs and work in silence,—this entire, pitiless, frightful, forced mechanism, this organized defiance, quickly disgusts the soul and tires the eye. The latter can rest only on cobblestones, shells, piles of iron, madriers, dry docks containing the naked hulls of vessels, and the grey walls of the prison, where a man leans out of the windows and tests the iron bars with a hammer.

Nature is absent and more completely banished from this place, than from any other spot on the face of the earth; everywhere can be seen denial and hatred of it, as much in the crowbar which demolishes the rocks, as in the sabre of the *garde-chiourme* who watches over the convicts.

Outside of the arsenal and the penitentiary, there is nothing but barracks, corps-de-garde, fortifications, ditches, uniforms, bayonets, sabres and drums. From morning until night, military music sounds under your windows, soldiers pass through the streets, come, go, and drill; the bugle sounds incessantly and the troops file past. You understand at once that the arsenal constitutes the real city and that the other is completely swallowed up by it. Everywhere and in every form reappear discipline, administration, ruled paper. Factitious symmetry and idiotic cleanliness are much admired. In the navy hospital for instance, the floors are so highly polished that a convalescent trying to walk on his mended leg would probably fall and break the other. But it looks nice. Between each ward is a yard, but the sun never shines in it, and the grass is carefully kept out. The kitchens are beautiful, but are situated so far from the main building that in winter the food must be cold before it reaches the patients. But who cares about them? Aren't the saucepans like polished suns? We saw a man who had broken his skull in falling from a vessel,,and who for eighteen hours had received no medical assistance whatsoever; but his sheets were immaculate, for the linen department is very well kept.

In the prison ward I was moved like a child by the sight of a litter of kittens playing on a convict's bed. He made them little paper balls, and they would chase them all over the bed-spread, and cling to its edges with their claws. Then he would turn them over, stroke them, kiss them and cuddle them to his heart. More than once, when he is put back to work and sits tired and depressed on his bench, he will dream of the quiet hours he spent alone with the little animals, and of the softness of their fur on his rough hands and the warmth of their little bodies against his breast. I believe, though, that the rules forbid this kind of recreation and that probably he had them through the kindness of the sister in charge.

But here, as well as elsewhere, rules have their exceptions, for, in the first place, the distinction of caste does not disappear (equality being a lie, even in the penitentiary). Delicately scented locks sometimes show beneath the numbered caps, just as the sleeve of the red blouse often reveals a cuff surrounding a well-kept hand. Moreover, special favours are shown toward certain professions, certain men. How have they been able, in spite of the law and the jealousy of their fellow-prisoners, to attain this eccentric position which makes them almost amateur convicts, and keep it without anybody trying to wrest it from them? At the entrance to the workshop, where boats are built, you will find a dentist's table filled with instruments. In a pretty frame on the wall, rows of plates are exhibited, and when you pass, the artist utters a little speech to advertise his ability. He stays in his place all day, polishing his instruments and stringing teeth; he can talk to visitors without feeling the restraint of being watched, be informed of what is going on in the medical world, and practise his profession like a licensed dentist. At the present time, I daresay, he must use ether. More than that, he may have pupils and give lectures. But the man who has the most enviable position of all is the curé Delacollonge.* He is the mediator between the convicts and the ban; the authorities use his ascendency over the prisoners, and they, in turn, address themselves to him when they want to obtain any favours.

He lives apart from the rest of them in a neat little room, has a man to wait on him, eats big bowls of Plougastel strawberries, takes his coffee and reads the newspapers.

If Delacollonge is the head of the penitentiary, Ambroise is its arm. Ambroise is a superb negro almost six feet tall, who would have made a fine servant for a sixteenth century man of quality. Heliogobalus must have kept some such fellow to furnish amusement for himself and his guests by strangling lions and fighting gladiators single-handed. His polished skin is quite black, with steely reflections; his body is well knit and as vigorous as a tiger's, and his teeth are so white that they almost frighten one.

King of the penitentiary by right of strength, all the convicts fear and admire him; his athletic reputation compels him to test every newcomer, and up to the present time, all these contests have turned out in his favour. He can bend iron rods over his knee, carry three men with one hand, and knock down eight by opening his arms; he eats three times as much as an ordinary man, for he has an enormous appetite and a heroic constitution.

---

* He strangled his mistress whose mutilated body was found floating in a sack on a pond. (See *Causes Célèbres.*)

When we saw him, he was watering the plants in the botanical garden. He is always hanging around the hot-house behind the plants and the palm-trees, digging the soil and cleansing the wood-work.

On Thursday, when the public is admitted, Ambroise receives his mistresses behind the boxed orange-trees; he has several of them, in fact, more than he wishes. He knows how to procure them, whether by his charms, his strength or his money, which he always carries in quantities about his person and spends lavishly whenever he wishes to enjoy himself. So he is very popular among a certain class of women, and the people who have put him where he is, have never perhaps been loved as much as Ambroise.

In the middle of the garden, in a little lake shaded by a willow-tree and bordered by plants, is a swan. With one stroke of its leg it can swim from one side of the pond to the other, and although it crosses it a hundred times a day and catches gold fishes to while away the time, it never thinks of wandering away.

Further on, in a line against the wall, are some cages for rare animals from foreign lands destined for the Museum of Paris. Most of the cages, however, were empty. In front of one, in a narrow grated yard, a convict was teaching a young wild-cat to obey commands like a dog. Hasn't this man had enough of slavery himself? Why does he torment this poor little beast? The lashes with which he is threatened he gives the wild-cat, which, some day, will probably take its revenge by jumping over the iron railing and killing the swan.

One moonlit evening, we decided to take a stroll through the streets known to be frequented by *filles de joie*. They are very numerous. The navy,

the artillery, the infantry, each has its own particular
streets, without mentioning the penitentiary, which
covers a whole district of the city. Seven parallel
streets ending at its walls, compose what is called
Keravel, and are filled by the mistresses of jailers and
convicts. They are old frame houses, crowded together, with every door and window closed tight.
No sound issues from them, nobody is seen coming
out, and there are no lights in the windows; at the
end of each street is a lamp-post which the wind
sways from side to side, thus making its long yellow
rays oscillate on the sidewalk. The rest of the
quarter is in absolute darkness. In the moonlight,
these silent houses with their uneven roofs projected
fantastic glimmerings.

When do they open? At unknown hours, at the
most silent time of the darkest nights. Then comes
the jailer who has slipped away from his watch, or
the convict who has managed to escape from the
prison, though sometimes they arrive together, aiding
and abetting each other; then, when daylight dawns,
the jailer turns his head away and nobody is the
wiser.

In the sailor's district, on the contrary, everything
is open and above-board. The disreputable houses
are full of noise and light; there is dancing and
shouting and fighting. On the ground floors, in
the low rooms, women in filmy attire sit on the
benches that line the white-washed walls lighted by
an oil lamp; others, in the doorway, beckon to you,
and their animated faces stand out in relief on the
background of the lighted resort, from which issues
the sound of clinking glasses and coarse caresses. You
can hear the kisses which fall on the opulent shoul-

ders of the women and the laughter of the girl who is sitting on some tanned sailor's lap, her unruly locks slipping from under her cap and her bare shoulders issuing from her chemise. The street is thronged, the place is packed, the door is wide open, anybody who wishes may go in. Men come and peep through the windows or talk in an undertone to some half-clad creature, who bends eagerly over their faces. Groups stand around and wait their turn. It is all quite informal and unrestrained.

Being conscientious travellers, and desiring to see and study everything at close range, we entered.

In a room papered in red, three or four girls were sitting at a round table, and a man with a cap on his head and a pipe in his mouth was reclining on the sofa; he bowed politely when we entered. The women wore Parisian dresses and were modest in their demeanour. The mahogany furniture was covered with red plush, the floor was polished and engravings of battles decorated the walls. O Virtue! you are beautiful, for very stupid is vice. The woman who was sitting by my side had hands which were sufficient in themselves to make a man forget her sex, and not knowing how to spend our time we treated the whole company to drinks. Then I lighted a cigar, stretched out on the divan, and, sad and depressed, while the voices of the women rose shrilly and the glasses were being drained, I said to myself:

Where is she? Where can she be? Is she dead to the world, and will men never see her again?

She was beautiful, in olden times, when she walked up the steps leading to the temple, when on her shell-like feet fell the golden fringe of her tunic, or when she lounged among Persian cushions, twirling her collar of cameos and chatting with the wise men and the philosophers.

She was beautiful when she stood naked on the threshold of her *cella* in the street of Suburra, under the rosin torchlight that blazed in the night, slowly chanting her Campanian lay, while from the Tiber came the refrains of the orgies.

She was beautiful, too, in her old house of the *Cité* behind the Gothic windows, among the noisy students and dissipated monks, when, without fear of the sergeants, they struck the oaken tables with their pewter mugs, and the worm-eaten beds creaked beneath the weight of their bodies.

She was beautiful when she leaned over the green cloth and coveted the gold of the provincials; then she wore high heels and had a small waist and a large wig which shed its perfumed powder on her shoulders, a rose over her ear and a patch on her cheek.

She was beautiful also among the goat-skins of the Cossacks and the English uniforms, pushing her way through the throngs of men and letting her bare shoulders dazzle them on the steps of the gambling houses, under the jewellers' windows, beneath the lights of the cafés, between starvation and wealth.

What are you regretting? I am regretting the *fille de joie*.

On the boulevard, one evening, I caught a glimpse of her as she passed under the gaslight, with watchful and eager eyes, dragging her feet over the sidewalk. I saw her pale face on the street-corner, while the rain wet the flowers in her hair, and heard her soft voice calling to the men, while her flesh shivered in her low-necked bodice.

It was her last day; after that she disappeared.

Fear not that she will ever return, for she is dead, quite dead! Her dress is made high, she has morals, objects to coarse language, and puts the sous she earns in a savings bank.

Cleared of her presence, the street has lost the only poetry it still retained; they have filtered the gutter and sorted the garbage.

In a little while, the mountebanks will also have disappeared, in order to make room for magnetic *séances* and reform banquets, and the rope-dancer with her spangled skirt and long balancing-pole will be as remote from us as the bayadère of the Ganges.

Of all that beautiful, glittering world as flighty as fancy itself, so melancholy and sonorous, so bitter and yet so gay, full of inward pathos and glaring sarcasms, where misery was warm and grace was sad, the last vestige of a lost age, a distant race, which, we are told, came from the other end of the earth and brought us in the tinkling of its bells the echo and vague memory of idolised joys; some covered wagon moving slowly along the road, with rolled tents on its roof and muddy dogs beneath it, a man in a yellow jacket, selling *muscade* in tin cups, the poor marionnettes in the Champs-Elysées, and the mandolin players who visit the cafés in the outskirts of the city, are all that is left.

Since then, it is true, we have had a number of farces of a higher class of humour. But is the new as good as the old? Do you prefer Tom Thumb or the Museum of Versailles?

On a wooden stand that formed a balcony around a square tent of grey canvas, a man in a blouse was beating a drum; behind him was a big painted sign representing a sheep and a cow, and some ladies, gentlemen, and soldiers. The animals were the two young phenomena from Guérande, with one arm and four shoulders. Their exhibitor, or editor, was shouting himself hoarse and announcing that besides these two beautiful things, battles between wild beasts would take place at once. Under the wooden stand stood a donkey and three bears, and the barking of the dogs, which proceeded from the interior of the tent, mingled with the beating of the drum, the shouts of the owner of the two phenomena and the cries of another fellow who was not as jovial and fat as the former, but tall and lanky, with a funereal expression and ragged clothes. This was the partner; they had met on the road and had combined their shows. The lean one contributed his bears, his dogs and his donkey, while the fat man brought his two phenomena and a grey felt hat which was used in their performance.

The theatre was roofless and its walls were of grey canvas; they fluttered in the wind and would have blown down had it not been for the poles which held them. Along the sides of the ring was a railing, behind which was the audience, and in a reserved corner we perceived the two phenomena nibbling at a bundle of hay half concealed by a gorgeous blanket. In the middle of the ring a high post was sunk in the ground, and here and there, attached to smaller posts, were dogs, barking and tugging at their chains. The men continued to shout and beat the drum, the bears growled, and the crowd began to file in.

First they brought out a poor, half-paralyzed bear, which seemed considerably bored. It wore a muzzle and had a big collar with an iron chain around its neck, a rope in its nose, to make it obey commands

promptly, and a sort of leather hood over its ears.
They tied bruin to the centre post, and the barks
grew louder and fiercer. The dogs stood up, a bris-
tling, scratching crew, their hind-quarters elevated,
their snouts near the ground, their legs spread, while
their masters stood in opposite corners of the ring
and yelled at them in order to increase their ferocity.
They let three bull-dogs go and the brutes rushed at
the bear, which began to dodge around the post. The
dogs followed, crowding and barking; sometimes the
bear would upset them and trample them with its
huge paws, but they would immediately scramble to
their feet and make a dash for its head, clinging to
its neck so that it was unable to shake off their
wriggling bodies. With watchful eye, the two masters waited the moment when it looked as if the bear
would be strangled; then they rushed at the dogs,
tore them away, pulled their necks and bit their tails
to make them unlock their jaws. The brutes whined
with pain, but they would not let go. The bear strug-
gled to free itself from the dogs, the dogs bit the bear,
and the men bit the dogs. One young bull-dog especially, was remarkable for its ferocity; it clung to the
bear's back and would not let go, though they chewed
and bent its tail, and lacerated its ears. The men were
compelled to get a mattock to loosen its jaws. When
they had all been disentangled, everyone took a rest;
the bear lay down on the ground, the gasping dogs
hung their tongues out, and the perspiring men pulled
the hairs from between their teeth, while the dust that
had arisen during the fight scattered in the atmosphere
and settled on the heads of the spectators.

Two more bears were led into the ring, and one
acted the gardener of the fable, went on a hunting

trip, waltzed, took off its hat, and played dead. After this performance came the donkey. But it defended itself well; its kicks sent the dogs flying through the air like balloons; with its tail between its legs and its ears back, it ran around the ring trying to get its foes under its forelegs while they endeavoured to run around it and fasten their teeth in its throat. When the men finally rescued it, it was completely winded and shaking with fright; it was covered with drops of blood which trickled down its legs (on which repeated wounds had left scars), and, mingling with sweat, moistened its worn hoofs.

But the best of the performance was the general fight between the dogs; all took part in it, the big and the little ones, the bull-dogs, the sheep-dogs, the white ones, the black ones, the spotted ones, and the russet variety. Fully fifteen minutes were spent in bringing them to the proper pitch of excitement. The owners held them between their legs and pointing their heads in the direction of their adversaries, would knock them together violently. The thin man, especially, worked with great gusto. With much effort he succeeded in producing a ferocious, hoarse chest-note that maddened the whole irritated pack. As serious as an orchestra leader, he would absorb the discordant harmony, and direct and strengthen its emission; but when the brutes were let loose and the howling band tore one another to pieces, he would be in a frenzy of enthusiasm and delight. He would applaud and bark and stamp his feet and imitate all the motions of the dogs; he would have enjoyed biting and being bitten, would gladly have been a dog himself with a snout, so that he could wallow in the dust and blood, and sink his teeth in the hairy

skins and warm flesh, and enjoy the fray to his
heart's content.

There was a critical moment when all the dogs,
one on top of another, formed a wriggling mass of
legs, backs, tails and ears, which oscillated to and
fro in the ring without separating, and in another instant had torn down the railing and threatened to
harm the two young phenomena. The owner's face
paled and he hastily sprang forward, while his partner rushed to his side. Then tails were bitten, and
kicks and blows were distributed right and left!
They grabbed the dogs everywhere, pulled them away
and flung them over their shoulders like bundles of
hay. It was all over in a second, but I had seen the
moment when the two young phenomena were near
being reduced to chopped meat, and I trembled for
the safety of the arm which grows on their back.

Flustered, no doubt, by their narrow escape, they
did not care to be shown off. The cow backed and
the sheep bucked; but finally the green blanket with
yellow fringe was removed and their appendage was
exhibited to the public, and then the performance
ended. . . .

CHAPTER IX

AT THE light-house of Brest. Here the Old World ends. This is its most advanced point; its farthest limit. Behind you spread Europe and Asia; before you lies the entire ocean. As great as space appears to our eye, does it not always seem limited as soon as we know that it has a boundary? Can you not see from our shores, across the Channel, the streets of Brighton and the fortresses of Provence; do you not always think of the Mediterranean as an immense blue lake ensconced in rocks, with promontories covered with falling monuments, yellow sands, swaying palm-trees and curved bays? But here nothing stops your eye. Thought can fly as rapidly as the winds, spread out, divagate, and lose itself, without finding anything but water, or perhaps vague America, nameless islands, or some country with red fruits, humming-birds and savages; or the silent twilight of the pole, with its spouting whales; or the great cities lighted by coloured glass, Japan with its porcelain roofs, and China with its sculptured staircases and its pagodas decorated with golden bells.

(87)

Thus does the mind people and animate this infinity, of which it tires so soon, in order that it may appear less vast. One cannot think of the desert without its caravans, of the ocean without its ships, of the bowels of the earth without evoking the treasures that they are supposed to conceal.

We returned to Conquet by way of the cliff. The breakers were dashing against its foot. Driven by a sea-breeze, they would come rushing in, strike the rocks and cover them with rippling sheets of water. Half an hour later, in a *char-à-banc* drawn by two sturdy little horses, we reached Brest, which we left with pleasure two days afterwards. When you leave the coast and approach the Channel, the country undergoes a marked change; it becomes less wild, less Celtic; the dolmens become scarcer, the flats diminish as the wheat fields grow more numerous, and, little by little, one reaches the fertile land of Léon, which is, as M. Pitre-Chevalier has gracefully put it, "the Attica of Brittany."

Landerneau is a place where there is an elm-tree promenade, and where we saw a frightened dog running through the streets with a pan attached to its tail.

In order to go to the Château de la Joyeuse-Garde, one must first follow the banks of the Eilorn and then walk through a forest, in a hollow where few persons go. Sometimes, when the underwood thins out and meadows appear between the branches, one catches sight of a boat sailing up the river.

Our guide preceded us at quite a distance. Alone together we trod the good old earth, flecked with bunches of purple heather and fallen leaves. The air was perfumed with the breath of violets and strawberries; slender ferns spread over the trunks of the trees. It was warm; even the moss was hot. A cuckoo, hidden in the foliage, now and then gave out its long cry, and gnats buzzed in the glades. We walked on with a feeling of inward peace, and let our conversation touch on many subjects; we spoke of sounds and colours, of the masters and their works, and of the joys of the mind; we thought of different writings, of familiar pictures and poses; we recited aloud some wonderful verses, the beauty of which thrilled us so that we repeated the rhythm again and again, accentuating the words and cadencing them so that they were almost sung. Foreign landscapes and splendid figures rose before our mind's eye, and we dwelt with rapture on soft Asiatic nights with the moon shining on the cupolas; or our admiration was aroused by some sonorous name; or we delighted in the artlessness of some sentence standing out in relief in an ancient book.

Stretched out in the courtyard of Joyeuse-Garde, near the filled-up subterranean vaults, beneath the semi-circle of its unique ivy-covered arcade, we talked of Shakespeare and wondered whether the stars were inhabited.

Then we started off again, having given but a hasty glance at the crumbling home of good old Lancelot, the one a fairy stole from his mother and kept in a shining palace at the bottom of a lake. The dwarfs have disappeared, the drawbridge has flown away, and lizards now crawl where formerly the entrancing Geneviève dreamed of her lover gone to fight the giants in Trébizonde.

We went back through the same paths to the forest; the shadows were lengthening, the flowers and shrubs were hardly visible, and the blue peaks of the low mountains opposite seemed to grow taller against the fading sky. The river, which is bordered by artificial quays for half a mile outside the city, now becomes free to spread its waters at will over the meadow; its wide curve stretched far away into the distance, and the pools of water coloured by the setting sun looked like immense golden platters forgotten on the grass.

Till it reaches Roche-Maurice, the Eilorn follows the road, which winds around the foot of the rocky hills, the uneven eminences of which extend into the valley. We were riding in a gig driven by a boy who sat on one of the shafts. His hat had no strings and consequently blew off occasionally, and during his efforts to catch it, we had plenty of time to admire the landscape.

The Château de la Roche-Maurice is a real burgrave's castle, a vulture's nest on the top of a mountain. It is reached by an almost perpendicular slope along which great blocks of stone are strewn in place of steps. At the top is a wall built of huge stones laid one above another, and in the wall are large windows, through which the whole surrounding country can be viewed; the woods, the fields, the river, the long, white road, the mountains with their uneven peaks, and the great meadow, which separates them through the middle.

A crumbling flight of steps leads to a dilapidated tower. Here and there stones crop out among the grass, and the rock shows amid the stones. Sometimes it seems as if this rock assumed artificial shapes, and as if the ruins, on the contrary, by crumbling more and more, had taken on a natural appearance and gone back to original matter.

A whole side of the wall is covered with ivy; it begins at the bottom and spreads out in an inverted pyramid, the color of which grows darker towards the top. Through an aperture, the edges of which are concealed by the foliage, one can see a section of the blue sky.

It was in these parts that the famous dragon lived, which was killed in olden times by knight Derrien, who was returning from the Holy Land with his friend, Neventer. Derrien attacked it as soon as he had rescued the unfortunate Eilorn who, after giving over his slaves, his vassals and his servants (he had no one left but his wife and son), had thrown himself headlong from the top of the tower into the river; but the monster, mortally wounded, and bound by the sash of its conqueror, soon drowned itself in the sea, at Poulbeunzual,* like the crocodile of Batz island, which obeyed the behest of Saint Pol de Léon and drowned itself with the stole of the Breton saint wound around it. The gargoyle of Rouen met a similar fate with the stole of Saint Romain.

How beautiful those terrific old dragons were, with their gaping, fire-spitting jaws, their scales, their serpent-tails, their bat-wings, their lion-claws, their equine bodies and fantastic heads! And the knight who overpowered them was a wonderfully fine specimen of manhood! First, his horse grew frightened and reared, and his lance broke on the scales of the monster, whose fiery breath blinded him. Finally he alighted, and after a day's battle, succeeded in sinking his sword up to the hilt in the beast's

---

* A contraction of Poulbeuzanneval, the swamp where the beast was drowned.

belly.   Black blood flowed in streams from the wound, the audience escorted the knight home in triumph, and he became king and married a fair maiden.

But where did the dragons come from?   Are they a confused recollection of the monsters that existed before the flood?   Were they conceived from the contemplation of the carcasses of the ichthyosaurus and pteropod, and did the terror of men hear the sound of their feet in the tall grass and the wind howl when their voices filled the caves?   Are we not, moreover, in the land of fairies, in the home of the Knights of the Round Table and of Merlin, in the mythological birthplace of vanished epopees?   These, no doubt, revealed something of the old worlds which have become mythical, and told something of the cities that were swallowed up, of Is and Herbadilla, splendid and barbaric places, filled with the loves of their bewitching queens, but now doubly wiped out, first, by the ocean which has obliterated them and then by religion, which has cursed their memory.

There is much to be said on this subject.   And, indeed, what is there on which much cannot be said? It might perhaps be Landivisian, for even the most prolix man is obliged to be concise in his remarks, when there is a lack of matter.   I have noticed that good places are usually the ugliest ones.   They are like virtuous women; one respects them, but one passes on in search of others.   Here, surely, is the most productive spot of all Brittany; the peasants are not as poor as elsewhere, the fields are properly cultivated, the colza is superb, the roads are in good condition, and it is frightfully dreary.

Cabbages, turnips, beets and an enormous quantity of potatoes, all enclosed by ditches, cover the entire country from Saint Pol de Léon to Roscoff. They are forwarded to Brest, Rennes, and even to Havre; it is the industry of the place, and a large business is done with them.

Roscoff has a slimy beach and a narrow bay, and the surrounding sea is sprinkled with tiny black islands that rise like the backs of so many turtles.

The environs of Saint Pol are dreary and cheerless. The bleak tint of the flats mingles without transition with the paleness of the sky, and the short perspective has no large lines in its proportions, nor change of colour on the edges. Here and there, while strolling through the fields, you may come across some silent farm behind a grey stone wall, an abandoned manor deserted by its owners. In the yard the pigs are sleeping on the manure heap and the chickens are pecking at the grass that grows among the loose stones; the sculptured shield above the door has worn away under the action of rain and atmosphere. The rooms are empty and are used for storage purposes; the plaster on the ceiling is peeling off, and so are the remaining decorations, which, besides, have been tarnished by the cobwebs of the spiders one sees crawling around the joists. Wild mignonette has grown on the door of Kersalion; near the turret is a pointed window flanked by a lion and a Hercules, which stand out in bold relief on the wall like two gargoyles. At Kerland, I stumbled against a wolf-trap while I was ascending the large winding staircase. Ploughshares, rusted shovels, and jars filled with dried grain were scattered around the rooms or on the wide stone window-seats.

Kerouséré has retained its three turrets with machicolations; in the courtyard can still be seen the deep furrows of the trenches that have been filled up little by little, and are now on level with the ground; they are like the track of a bark, which spreads and spreads over the water till it finally disappears. From the platform of one of the towers (the others have pointed roofs), one can see the ocean between two low, wooded hills. The windows on the first floor are half stopped up, so as to keep the rain out; they look out into a garden enclosed by a high wall. The grass is covered with thistles and wheat grows in the flower-beds surrounded by rose-bushes.

A narrow path wends its way between a field where the ripe wheat sways in the breeze and a line of elm-trees growing on the edge of a ditch. Poppies gleamed here and there amongst the wheat; the ditch was edged with flowers, brambles, nettles, sweet-brier, long prickly stems, broad shining leaves, blackberries and purple digitalis, all of which mingled their colours and various foliage and uneven branches, and crossed their shadows on the grey dust like the meshes of a net.

When you have crossed a meadow where an old mill reluctantly turns its clogged wheel, you follow the wall by stepping on large stones placed in the water for a bridge; you soon come to the road that leads to Saint-Pol, at the end of which rises the slashed steeple of Kreisker; tall and slender, it dominates a tower decorated with a balustrade and produces a fine effect at a distance; but the nearer one gets to it, the smaller and uglier it becomes, till finally one finds that it is nothing more than an ordinary church with a portal devoid of statues. The cathedral also is built in a rather clumsy Gothic style, and is overloaded with ornaments and embroideries;

but there is one notable thing, at least, in Saint-Pol, and that is the *table d'hôte* of the inn.

The girl who waits on it has gold earrings dangling against her white neck and a cap with turned up wings, like Molière's soubrettes, and her sparkling blue eyes would incline anyone to ask her for something more than mere plates. But the guests! What guests! All *habitués!* At the upper end sat a creature in a velvet jacket and a cashmere waistcoat. He tied his napkin around the bottles that had been uncorked, in order to be able to distinguish them. He ladled the soup. On his left, sat a man in a light grey frock-coat, with the cuffs and collar trimmed with a sort of curly material representing fur; he ate with his hat on and was the professor of music at the local college. But he has grown tired of his profession and is anxious to find some place that would bring him from eight to twelve hundred francs at the most. He does not care so much about the salary, what he desires is the consideration that attaches to such a place. As he was always late, he requested that the courses be brought up again from the kitchen, and if he did not like them, he would send them back untouched; he sneezed and expectorated and rocked his chair and hummed and leaned his elbows on the table and picked his teeth.

Everybody respects him, the waitress admires everything he says, and is, I am sure, in love with him. The high opinion he has of himself shows in his smile, his speech, his gestures, his silence, and in his way of wearing his hair; it emanates from his entire obnoxious personality.

Opposite to us sat a grey-haired, plump man with red hands and thick, moist lips, who looked at us so persistently and annoyingly, while he masticated his food, that we felt like throwing the carafes at him. The other guests were insignificant and only contributed to the picture.

One evening the conversation fell upon a woman of the environs who had left her husband and gone to America with her lover, and who, the previous week, and passed through Saint-Pol on her way home, and had stopped at the inn. Everybody wondered at her audacity, and her name was accompanied by all sorts of unflattering epithets. Her whole life was passed in review by these people, and they all laughed contemptuously and insulted her and grew quite hot over the argument. They would have liked to have her there to tell her what they thought of her and see what she would say. Tirades against luxury, virtuous horror, moral maxims, hatred of wealth, words with a double meaning, shrugs, everything, in fact, was used to crush this woman, who, judging by the ferocity these ruffians displayed in their attacks, must have been pretty, refined, and charming. Our hearts beat indignantly in our breasts, and if we had taken another meal in Saint-Pol, I am sure that something would have happened.

CHAPTER X.

AINT-MALO, which is built right
on the ocean and is enclosed by
ramparts, looks like a crown of
stones, the gems of which are
the machicolations. The breakers
dash against its walls, and when the
tide is low they gently unfurl on the sand. Little
rocks covered with sea-weed dot the beach and look
like black spots on its light surface. The larger
ones, which are upright and smooth, support the
fortifications, thus making them appear higher than
they really are.

Above this straight line of walls, broken here and
there by a tower or the pointed ogive of a door, rise
the roofs of the houses with their open garret-windows, their gyrating weather-cocks, and their red
chimneys from which issue spirals of bluish smoke
that vanishes in the air.

Around Saint-Malo are a number of little barren
islands that have not a tree nor a blade of grass, but
only some old crumbling walls, great pieces of which
are hurled into the sea by each succeeding storm.

On the other side of the bay, opposite the city
and connected with dry land by a long pier, which

separates the port from the ocean, is Saint-Servan, a large, empty, almost deserted locality, which lies peacefully in a marshy meadow. At the entrance to Saint-Servan rise the four towers of the Château de Solidor, which are connected by curtains and are perfectly black from top to bottom. These alone are sufficient compensation for having made that extended circuit on the beach, under the broiling July sun, among the dock-yards and tar-pots and fires.

A walk around the city, over the ramparts, is one of the finest that can be taken. Nobody goes there. You can sit down in the embrasures of the cannons and dangle your feet over the abyss. In front of you lies the mouth of the Rance, which flows between two green hills, the coast, the islands, the rocks, and the ocean. The sentinel marches up and down behind you, and his even footsteps echo on the sonorous stones.

One evening we remained out for a long time. The night was beautiful, a true summer night, without a moon, but brilliant with stars and perfumed by the sea-breeze. The city was sleeping. One by one the lights went out in the windows, and the lighthouses shone red in the darkness, which was quite blue above us and glittering with myriads of twinkling stars. We could not see the ocean, but we could hear and smell it, and the breakers that lashed the walls flung drops of foam over us through the big apertures of the machicolations.

In one place, between the wall and the city houses, a quantity of cannon-balls are piled up in a ditch. From that point you can see these words written on the second floor of one of the dwellings: "Chateaubriand was born here."

Further on, the wall ends at the foot of a tower called Quiquengrogne; like its sister, La Générale, it is high, broad, and imposing, and is swelled in the middle like a hyperbola.

Though they are as good as new and absolutely intact, these towers would no doubt be improved if they lost some of their battlements in the sea and if ivy spread its kindly leaves over their tops. Indeed, do not monuments grow greater through recollection, like men and like passions? And are they not completed by death?

We entered the castle. The empty courtyard planted with a few sickly lime-trees was as silent as the courtyard of a monastery. The janitress went and obtained the keys from the commander. When she returned, she was accompanied by a pretty little girl who wished to see the strangers. Her arms were bare and she carried a large bunch of flowers. Her black curls escaped from beneath her dainty little cap, and the lace on her pantalettes rubbed against her kid shoes tied around the ankles with black laces. She ran up stairs in front of us beckoning and calling.

The staircase is long, for the tower is high. The bright daylight passes through the loop-holes like an arrow. When you put your head through one of these openings, you can see the ocean, which seems to grow wider and wider, and the crude colour of the sky, which seems to grow larger and larger, till you are afraid you will lose yourself in it. Vessels look like launches and their masts like walking-sticks. Eagles must think we look like ants. I wonder whether they really see us. Do they know that we have cities and steeples and triumphal arches?

When we arrived on the platform, and although the battlement reached to our chest, we could not help experiencing the sensation one always feels at a great height from the earth. It is a sort of voluptuous uneasiness mingled with fear and delight, pride and terror, a battle between one's mind and one's nerves. You feel strangely happy; you would like to jump, fly, spread out in the air and be supported by the wind; but your knees tremble and you dare not go too near the edge.

Still, one night, in olden times, men climbed this tower with ropes. But then, it is not astonishing for those times, for that wonderful sixteenth century, the epoch of fierce convictions and frantic loves! How the human instrument vibrated then in all its chords! How liberal-minded, productive, and active men were! Does not this phrase of Fénelon apply wonderfully well to that period: "A sight well calculated to delight the eye?" For, without making any reference to the foreground of the picture,—beliefs crumbling at their foundation like tottering mountains, newly discovered worlds, lost worlds brought to light again, Michael-Angelo beneath his dome, laughing Rabelais, observant Shakespeare, pensive Montaigne,—where can be found a greater development in passions, a greater violence in courage, a greater determination in willpower, in fine, a more complete expansion of liberty struggling against all native fatalities? And with what a bold relief the episode stands out in history, and still, how wonderfully well it fits in, thereby giving a glimpse of the dazzling brightness and broad horizons of the period. Faces, living faces, pass before your eyes. You meet them only once; but you think of them long afterwards, and endeavour to contemplate them in order that they may be impressed more deeply upon your mind. Was not the type of the old soldiers whose race disappeared around 1598, at the taking of Vervins, fine and terrible? It was a type represented by men like Lamouche, Heurtand de Saint-Offange, and La Tremblaye, who came back holding the heads of his enemies in his hand; also La Fontenelle, of whom so much has been said. They were men of iron, whose hearts were no softer than their swords, and who, attracting hundreds of energies which they directed with their own, entered towns at night, galloping madly at the heads of their companies, equipped corsairs, burned villages, and were dealt with like kings! Who has thought of depicting those violent governors of the provinces, who slaughtered the people recklessly, committed rapes and swept in gold, like D'Epernon, an atrocious tyrant in Provence and a perfumed courtier at the Louvre; like Montluc, who strangled Huguenots with his own hands, or Baligui, the king of Cambrai, who read Machiavel in order to copy the Valentinois, and whose wife went to war on horseback, wearing a helmet and a cuirass.

One of the forgotten men of the period, or at at least one of those whom most historians mention only slightly, is the Duke of Mercœur, the intrepid enemy of Henri IV, who defied him longer than Mayenne, the Ligue, and Philip II. Finally he was disarmed, that is, won over and appeased (by terms that were such that twenty-three articles of the treaty were not disclosed); then, not knowing what to do, he enlisted in the Hungarian army and fought the Turks. One day, with five thousand men, he attacked a whole army, and, beaten again, returned to

France and died of the fever in Nuremberg, at the age of forty-four.

Saint-Malo put me in mind of him. He always tried to get it, but he never could succeed in making it his subject or his ally. They wished to fight on their own account, and to do business through their own resources, and although they were really *ligueurs,* they spurned the duke as well as the Béarnais.

When De Fontaines, the governor of the city, informed them of the death of Henri III, they refused to recognize the King of Navarre. They armed themselves and erected barricades; De Fontaines intrenched himself in the castle and everybody kept upon the defensive. Little by little, the people encroached upon him; first, they requested him to declare that he was willing to maintain their franchises. De Fontaines complied in the hope of gaining time. The following year (1589), they chose four generals who were independent of the governor. A year later, they obtained permission to stretch chains. De Fontaines acceded to everything. The king was at Laval and he was waiting for him. The time was close at hand when he would be able to take revenge for all the humiliations he had suffered, and all the concessions he had been forced to make. But he precipitated matters and was discovered. When the people of Saint-Malo reminded him of his promises, he replied that if the king presented himself, he (De Fontaines) would let him enter the city. When they learned this, they decided to act.

The castle had four towers. It was the highest one, La Générale, the one on which De Fontaines relied the most, which they climbed. These bold attempts were not infrequent, as proved by the ascension of

the cliffs of Fécamp by Bois-Rosé, and the attack of
the Château de Blein, by Guébriant.

The rebels connived and assembled during several
evenings at the place of a certain man named Frotet,
sieur de La Lanbelle; they entered into an understand-
ing with a Scotch gunner, and one dark night they
armed themselves, went out to the rampart, let themselves down with ropes and approached the foot of
La Générale.

There they waited. Soon a rustling sound was
heard on the wall, and a ball of thread was lowered,
to which they fastened their rope ladder. The ladder
was then hoisted to the top of the tower and attached to the end of a culverin which was levelled
in an embrasure of the battlement.

Michel Frotet was the first to ascend, and after
him came Charles Anselin, La Blissais and the others.
The night was dark and the wind whistled; they had
to climb slowly, to hold their daggers between
their teeth and feel for the rungs of the ladder with
their hands and feet. Suddenly (they were midway
between the ground and the top), they felt themselves going down; the rope had slipped. But they
did not utter a sound; they remained motionless.
Their weight had caused the culverin to tip forward;
it stopped on the edge of the embrasure and they
slowly resumed their ascension and arrived one after
another on the platform of the tower.

The sleepy sentinels did not have time to give
the alarm. The garrison was either asleep or playing
dice on the drums. A panic seized the soldiers and
they fled to the dungeon. The conspirators pursued
them and attacked them in the hallways, on the
staircase, and in the rooms, crushing them between

the doors and slaughtering them mercilessly. Meanwhile the townspeople arrived to lend assistance; some put up ladders, and entered the tower without encountering any resistance and plundered it. La Pérandière, lieutenant of the castle, perceiving La Blissais, said to him: "This, sir, is a most miserable night." But La Blissais impressed upon him that this was not the time for conversation. The Count of Fontaines had not made his appearance. They went in search of him, and found him lying dead across the threshold of his chamber, pierced by a shot from an arquebuse that one of the townspeople had fired at him, as he was about to go out, escorted by a servant bearing a light. "Instead of rushing to face the danger," says the author of this account,* "he had dressed as leisurely as if he were going to a wedding, without leaving one shoulder-knot untied."

This outbreak in Saint-Malo, which so greatly harmed the king, did not in the least benefit the Duke de Mercœur. He had hoped that the people would accept a governor from his hands, his son, for example, a mere child, for that would have meant himself, but they obstinately refused to listen to it. He sent troops to protect them, but they refused to let them enter, and the soldiers were compelled to take lodgings outside of the city.

Still, in spite of all this, they had not become more royalist, for some time later, having arrested the Marquis of La Noussaie and the Viscount of Denoual, it cost the former twelve thousand crowns to get out of prison and the latter two thousand.

---

*Josselin Frotet, sieur de La Lanbelle, at whose place the rebels congregated before the escalade. (Note on the manuscript of G. F.)

Then, fearing that Pont-Brient would interrupt commercial relations with Dinan and the other cities in the Ligue, they attacked and subjected it.

Presuming that their bishop, who was the temporal master of the city, might be likely to deprive them of the freedom they had just acquired, they put him in prison and kept him there for a year.

The conditions at which they finally accepted Henri IV are well-known: they were to take care of themselves, not be obliged to receive any garrison, be exempt from taxes for six years, etc.

Situated between Brittany and Normandy, this little people seems to have the tenacity and granite-like resistance of the former and the impulses and dash of the latter. Whether they are sailors, writers, or travellers on foreign seas, their predominant trait is audacity; they have violent natures which are almost poetical in their brutality, and often narrow in their obstinacy. There is this resemblance between these two sons of Saint-Malo, Lamennais and Broussais: they were always equally extreme in their systems and employed their latter years in fighting what they had upheld in the earlier part of their life.

In the city itself are little tortuous streets edged with high houses and dirty fishmongers' shops. There are no carriages or luxuries of any description; everything is as black and reeking as the hold of a ship. A sort of musty smell, reminiscent of Newfoundland, salt meat, and long sea voyages pervades the air.

"The watch and the round are made every night with big English dogs, which are let loose outside of the city by the man who is in charge of them, and it is better not to be in their vicinity at that time. But when morning comes, they are led back to a place in the city where they shed all their ferocity which, at night, is so great."*

Barring the disappearance of this four-legged police which at one time devoured M. du Mollet, the existence of which is confirmed by a contemporaneous text, the exterior of things has changed but little, no doubt, and even the civilized people living in Saint-Malo admit that it is very much behind the times.

The only picture we noticed in the church is a large canvas that represents the battle of Lépante and is dedicated to Nôtre-Dame des Victoires, who can be seen floating above the clouds. In the foreground, all Christianity, together with crowned kings and princesses, is kneeling. The two armies can be seen in the background. The Turks are being hurled into the sea and the Christians stretch their arms towards heaven.

The church is ugly, has no ornamentation, and looks almost like a Protestant house of worship. I noticed very few votive offerings, a fact that struck me as being rather peculiar in this place of sea perils. There are no flowers nor candles in the chapels, no bleeding hearts nor bedecked Virgin, nothing, in fact, of all that which causes M. Michelet to wax indignant.

Opposite the ramparts, at a stone's throw from the city, rises the little island of Grand-Bay. There, can be found the tomb cf Chateaubriand; that white spot cut in the rock is the place he has designated for his body.

We went there one evening when the tide was low and the sun setting in the west. The water

---

* D'Argentré, *Hist. de Bretagne*, p. 62.

was still trickling over the sand. At the foot of the island, the dripping sea-weed spread out like the hair of antique women over a tomb.

The island is deserted; sparse grass grows in spots, mingled here and there with tufts of purple flowers and nettles. On the summit is a dilapidated case-mate, with a courtyard enclosed by crumbling walls. Beneath this ruin, and half-way up the hill, is a space about ten feet square, in the middle of which rises a granite slab surmounted by a Latin cross. The tomb comprises three pieces: one for the socle, one for the slab, and another for the cross.

Chateaubriand will rest beneath it, with his head turned towards the sea; in this grave, built on a rock, his immortality will be like his life — deserted and surrounded by tempests. The centuries and the break-ers will murmur a long time around his great memory; the breakers will dash against his tomb during storms, or on summer mornings, when the white sails unfold and the swallow arrives from across the seas; they will bring him the melancholy voluptuousness of far-away horizons and the caressing touch of the sea-breeze. And while time passes and the waves of his native strand swing back and forth between his cradle and his grave, the great heart of René, grown cold, will slowly crumble to dust to the eternal rhythm of this never-ceasing music.

We walked around the tomb and touched it, and looked at it as if it contained its future host, and sat down beside it on the ground.

The sky was pink, the sea was calm, and there was a lull in the breeze. Not a ripple broke the motionless surface of ocean on which the setting sun shed its golden light. Blue near the coast and mingled with the evening mist, the sea was scarlet everywhere else and deepened into a dark red line on the horizon. The sun had no rays left; they had fallen from its face and drowned their brilliancy in the water, on which they seemed to float. The red disc set slowly, robbing the sky of the pink tinge it had diffused over it, and while both the sun and the delicate color were wearing away, the pale blue shades of night crept over the heavens. Soon the sun touched the ocean and sank into it to the middle. For a moment it appeared cut in two by the horizon; the upper half remained firm, while the under one vacillated and lengthened; then it finally disappeared; and when the reflection died away from the place where the fiery ball had gone down, it seemed as if a sudden gloom had spread over the sea.

The shore was dark. The light in one of the windows in a city house, which a moment before was bright, presently went out. The silence grew deeper, though sounds could be heard. The breakers dashed against the rocks and fell back with a roar; long-legged gnats sang in our ears and disappeared with a buzzing of their transparent wings, and the indistinct voices of the children bathing at the foot of the ramparts reached us, mingled with their laughter and screams.

Young boys came out of the water, and, stepping gingerly on the pebbles, ran up the beach to dress. When they attempted to put on their shirts, the moist linen clung to their wet shoulders and we could see their white torsos wriggling with impatience, while their heads and arms remained concealed and the sleeves flapped in the wind like flags.

A man with his wet hair falling straight around

his neck, passed in front of us. His dripping body shone. Drops trickled from his dark, curly beard, and he shook his head so as to let the water run out of his locks. His broad chest was parted by a stubby growth of hair that extended between his powerful muscles. It heaved with the exertion of swimming and imparted an even motion to his flat abdomen, which was as smooth as ivory where it joined the hips. His muscular thighs were set above slender knees and fine legs ending in arched feet, with short heels and spread toes. He walked slowly over the beach.

How beautiful is the human form when it appears in its original freedom, as it was created in the first day of the world! But where are we to find it, masked as it is and condemned never to reappear. That great word, Nature, which humanity has repeated sometimes with idolatry and sometimes with fear, which philosophers have sounded and poets have sung, how it is being lost and forgotten! If there are still here and there in the world, far from the pushing crowd, some hearts which are tormented by the constant search of beauty, and forever feeling the hopeless need of expressing what cannot be expressed and doing what can only be dreamed, it is to Nature, as to the home of the ideal, that they must turn. But how can they? By what magic will they be able to do so? Man has cut down the forests, has conquered the seas, and the clouds that hover over the cities are produced by the smoke that rises from the chimneys. But, say others, do not his mission and his glory consist in going forward and attacking the work of God, and encroaching upon it? Man denies His work, he ruins it, crushes it, even in his own body, of which he is ashamed and which he conceals like a crime.

Man having thus become the rarest and most difficult thing in the world to know (I am not speaking of his heart, O moralists!), it follows that the artist ignores his shape as well as the qualities that render it beautiful. Where is the poet, nowadays, even amongst the most brilliant, who knows what a woman is like? Where could the poor fellow ever have seen any? What has he ever been able to learn about them in the salons; could he see through the corset and the crinoline?

Better than all the rhetoric in the world, the plastic art teaches those who study it the gradation of proportions, the fusion of planes, in a word, harmony. The ancient races, through the very fact of their existence, left the mark of their noble attitudes and pure blood on the works of the masters. In Juvenal, I can hear confusedly the death-rattles of the gladiators; Tacitus has sentences that resemble the drapery of a laticlave, and some of Horace's verses are like the body of a Greek slave, with supple undulations, and short and long syllables that sound like crotala.

But why bother about these things? Let us not go so far back, and let us be satisfied with what is manufactured. What is wanted nowadays is rather the opposite of nudity, simplicity and truth? Fortune and success will fall to the lot of those who know how to dress and clothe facts! The tailor is the king of the century and the fig-leaf is its symbol; laws, art, politics, all things, appear in tights! Lying freedom, plated furniture, water-colour pictures, why! the public loves this sort of thing! So let us give it all it wants and gorge the fool!

CHAPTER XI

Mont Saint-Michel.

THE road from Pontorson to the Mont Saint-Michel is wearying on account of the sand. Our post-chaise (for we also travel by post-chaise), was disturbed every now and then by a number of carts filled with the grey soil which is found in these parts and which is transported to some place and utilised as manure. They became more numerous as we approached the sea, and defiled for several miles until we finally saw the deserted strand whence they came. On this white surface, with its conical heaps of earth resembling huts, the fluctuating line of carts reminded us of an emigration of barbarians deserting their native heath.

The empty horizon stretches out, spreads, and finally mingles its greyish flats with the yellow sand of the beach. The ground becomes firmer and a salt breeze fans your cheeks; it looks like a vast desert from which the waters have receded. Long, flat strips of sand, superposed indefinitely in indistinct planes, ripple like shadows, and the wind playfully designs huge arabesques on their surfaces. The sea lies far away, so far, in fact, that its roar cannot be heard, though we could distinguish a sort of vague, aërial, imperceptible murmur, like the voice of the solitude, which perhaps was only the effect produced by the intense silence.

Opposite us rose a large round rock with embattled walls and a church on its top; enormous counterparts resting on a steep slope support the sides of the edifice. Rocks and wild shrubs are strewn over the incline. Half-way up the slope are a few houses, which show above the white line of the wall and are dominated by the brown church; thus some bright colours are interspersed between the two plain tints.

The post-chaise drove ahead of us and we followed it, guiding ourselves by the tracks of the wheels; finally it disappeared in the distance, and we could distinguish only its hood, which looked like some big crab crawling over the sand.

Here and there a swift current of water compelled us to move farther up the beach. Or we would suddenly come upon pools of slime with ragged edges framed in sand.

Beside us walked two priests who were also going to the Mont Saint-Michel. As they were afraid of soiling their new cassocks, they gathered them up around their legs when they jumped over the little streams. Their silver buckles were grey with mud, and their wet shoes gaped and threw water at every step they took.

Meantime the Mount was growing larger. With one sweep of the eye we were able to take in the whole panorama, and could see distinctly the tiles on

the roofs, the bunches of nettles on the rocks, and, a little higher, the green shutters of a small window that looks out into the governor's garden.

The first door, which is narrow and pointed, opens on a sort of pebble road leading to the ocean; on the worn shield over the second door, undulating lines carved in the stone seem to represent water; on both sides of the doors are enormous cannons composed of iron bars connected by similar circular bands. One of them has retained a cannon-ball in its mouth; they were taken from the English in 1423, by Louis d'Estouteville, and have remained here four hundred years.

Five or six houses built opposite one another compose the street; then the line breaks, and they continue down the slopes and stairs leading to the castle, in a sort of haphazard fashion.

In order to reach the castle, you first go up to the curtain, the wall of which shuts out the view of the ocean from the houses below. Grass grows between the cracked stones and the battlements. The rampart continues around the whole island and is elevated by successive platforms. When you have passed the watch-house, which is situated between the two towers, you see a little straight flight of steps; when you climb them, the roofs of the houses, with their dilapidated chimneys, gradually grow lower and lower. You can see the washing hung out to dry on poles fastened to the garret-windows, or a tiny garden baking in the sun between the roof of one house and the ground-floor of another, with its parched leeks drooping their leaves over the grey soil; but the other side of the rock, the side that faces the ocean, is barren and deserted, and so steep that the shrubs that grow there have a hard time to remain where they are and look as if they were about to topple over every minute.

When you are standing up there, enjoying as much space as the human eye can possibly encompass and looking at the ocean and the horizon of the coast, which forms an immense bluish curve, or at the wall of La Merveille with its thirty-six huge counterparts upreared on a perpendicular cliff, a laugh of admiration parts your lips, and you suddenly hear the sharp noise of the weaving-looms. The people manufacture linen, and the shrill sound of the shuttles produces a very lively racket.

Between two slender towers, which represent the uplifted barrels of two cannons, is the entrance to the castle, a long, arched hallway, at the end of which is a flight of stone steps. The middle of the hall is always dark, being insufficiently lighted by two skylights one of which is at the bottom of the hall and the other at the top, between the interval of the drawbridge; it is like a subterranean vault.

The guard-room is at the head of the stairs as you enter. The voice of the sergeants and the clicking of the guns re-echoed along the walls. They were beating a drum.

Meanwhile a *garde-chiourme* returned with our passports, which M. le gouverneur had wished to see; then he motioned us to follow him; he opened doors, drew bolts, and led us through a maze of halls, vaults and staircases. Really, one can lose oneself in this labyrinth, for a single visit does not enable you to understand the complicated plan of these combined buildings, where a fortress, a church, an abbey, a prison and a dungeon, are mingled, and where you can find every style of architecture, from the Romance of the eleventh century to the bewildering Gothic of the sixteenth. We could catch only a glimpse of the knights' hall, which has been converted into a loom-room and is for this reason barred to the public. We saw only four rows of columns supporting a ceiling ornamented with salient mouldings; they were decorated with clover leaves. The monastery is built over this hall, at an altitude of two hundred feet above the sea level. It is composed of a quadrangular gallery formed by a triple line of small granite, tufa, or stucco columns. Acanthus, thistles, ivy, and oak-leaves wind around their caps; between each mitred ogive is a cut-out rose; this gallery is the place where the prisoners take the air.

The cap of the *garde-chiourme* now passes along these walls where, in olden times, passed the shaved heads of industrious friars; and the wooden shoes of the prisoners click on the slabs that used to be swept by the trailing robes of monks and trodden by their heavy leather sandals.

The church has a Gothic choir and a Romance nave, and the two architectures seem to vie with each other in majesty and elegance. In the choir, the arches of the windows are pointed, and are as lofty as the aspirations of love; in the nave, the arcades open their semi-circles roundly, and columns as straight as the trunk of a palm-tree mount along the walls. They rest on square pedestals, are crowned with acanthus leaves, and continue in powerful mouldings that curve beneath the ceiling and help support it.

It was noon. The bright daylight poured in through the open door and rippled over the dark sides of the building.

The nave, which is separated from the choir by a green curtain, is filled with tables and benches, for it is used also as a dining-hall. When mass is celebrated, the curtain is drawn and the condemned men may be present at divine service without removing their elbows from the table. It is a novel idea.

In order to enlarge the platform by twelve yards on the western side of the church, the latter itself has been curtailed; but as it was necessary to reconstruct some sort of entrance, one architect closed the nave by a façade in Greek style; then, perhaps, feeling remorseful, or desiring (a presumption which will be accepted more readily), to embellish his work still further, he afterwards added some columns "which imitate fairly well the architecture of the eleventh century," says the notice. Let us be silent and bow our heads. Each of the arts has its own particular leprosy, its mortal ignominy that eats its face away. Painting has the family group, music the ballad, literature the criticism, and architecture the architect.

The prisoners were walking around the platform, one after another, silent, with folded arms, and in the beautiful order we had the opportunity to admire at Fontevrault. They were the patients of the hospital ward taking the air.

Tottering along with the file was one who lifted his feet higher than the rest and clung to the coat of the man ahead of him. He was blind. Poor, miserable wretch! God prevents him from seeing and his fellow-men forbid him to speak!

The following day, when the tide had again receded from the beach, we left the Mount under a broiling sun which heated the hood of the carriage and made the horses sweat. They only walked; the harness creaked and the wheels sank deep into the sand. At the end of the beach, when grass appeared again, I put my eye to the little window that is in the back of every carriage, and bade goodbye to Mont Saint-Michel.

CHAPTER XII.

A LETTER from the Viscount Vésin was to gain us entrance to the castle. So as soon as we arrived, we called on the steward, M. Corvesier. They ushered us into a large kitchen where a young lady in black, marked by smallpox and wearing horn spectacles over her prominent eyes, was stemming currants. The kettle was on the fire and they were crushing sugar with bottles. It was evident that we were intruding. After several minutes had elapsed, we were informed that M. Corvesier was confined to his bed with a fever and was very sorry that he could not be of any service to us, but sent us his regards. In the meantime, his clerk, who had just come in from an errand, and who was lunching on a glass of cider and a piece of buttered bread, offered to show us the castle. He put his napkin down, sucked his teeth, lighted his pipe, took a bunch of keys from the wall and started ahead of us through the village.

After following a long wall, we entered through an old door into a silent farm-yard. Silica here and there shows through the beaten ground, on which

(118)

grows a little grass soiled by manure. There was nobody around and the stable was empty. In the barns some chickens were roosting on the poles of the wagons, with their heads under their wings. Around the buildings, the sound of our footsteps was deadened by the dust accumulated from the straw in the lofts.

Four large towers connected by curtains showed battlements beneath their pointed roofs; the openings in the towers, like those in the main part of the castle, are small, irregular windows, which form uneven black squares on the grey stones. A broad stoop, comprising about thirty steps, reaches to the first floor, which has become the ground-floor of the interior apartments, since the trenches have been filled up.

The yellow wall-flower does not grow here, but instead, one finds nettles and lentisks, greenish moss and lichens. To the left, next to the turret, is a cluster of chestnut-trees reaching up to the roof and shading it.

After the key had been turned in the lock and the door pushed open with kicks, we entered a dark hallway filled with boards and ladders and wheelbarrows.

This passage led into a little yard enclosed by the thick interior walls of the castle. It was lighted from the top like a prison yard. In the corners, drops of humidity dripped from the stones. We opened another door. It led into a large, empty, sonorous hall; the floor was cracked in a hundred places, but there was fresh paint on the wainscoting.

The green forest opposite sheds a vivid reflection on the white walls, through the large windows of the castle. There is a lake and underneath the windows were clusters of lilacs, petunia-blossoms and acacias, which have grown pell-mell in the former parterre, and cover the hill that slopes gradually to the road, following the banks of the lake and then continuing through the woods.

The great, deserted hall, where the child who afterwards wrote *René*, used to sit and gaze out of the windows, was silent. The clerk smoked his pipe and expectorated on the floor. His dog, which had followed him, hunted for mice, and its nails clicked on the pavement.

We walked up the winding stairs. Moss covers the worn stone steps. Sometimes a ray of light, passing through a crack in the walls, strikes a green blade and makes it gleam in the dark like a star.

We wandered through the halls, through the towers, and over the narrow curtain with its gaping machicolations, which attract the eye irresistibly to the abyss below.

On the second floor is a small room which looks out into the inside courtyard and has a massive oak door that closes with a latch. The beams of the ceiling (you can touch them), are rotten from age; the whitewashed walls show their lattice-work and are covered with big spots; the window-panes are obscured by cobwebs and their frames are buried in dust. This used to be Chateaubriand's room. It faces the West, towards the setting sun.

We continued; when we passed in front of a window or a loop-hole, we warmed ourselves in the warm air coming from without, and this sudden transition rendered the ruins all the more melancholy and cheerless. The floors of the apartments are rotting away, and daylight enters through the fireplaces along the blackened slab where rain has left long green streaks. The golden flowers on the drawing-room ceiling are falling off, and the shield that surmounts the mantelpiece is broken into bits. While we were looking around, a flight of birds entered, flew around for a few minutes and passed out through the chimney.

In the evening, we went to the lake. The meadow has encroached upon it and will soon cover it entirely, and wheat will grow in the place of pond-lilies. Night was falling. The castle, flanked by its four turrets and framed by masses of green foliage, cast a dark shadow over the village. The setting sun made the great mass appear black; the dying rays touched the surface of the lake and then melted in the mist on the purplish top of the silent forest.

We sat down at the foot of an oak and opened *René*. We faced the lake where he had often watched the nimble swallow on the bending reeds; we sat in the shadow of the forest where he had often pursued rainbows over the dripping hills; we harkened to the rustling of the leaves and the whisperings of the water that had added their murmur to the sad melody of his youth. As the darkness gathered on the pages of the book, the bitterness of its words went to our hearts, and we experienced a sensation of mingled melancholy and sweetness.

A wagon passed in the road, and the wheels sank in the deep tracks. A smell of new-mown hay pervaded the air. The frogs were croaking in the marshes. We went back.

The sky was heavy and a storm raged all night. The front of a neighbouring house was illumined and flared like a bonfire at every flash of lightning. Gasping, and tired of tossing on my bed, I arose, lighted a candle, opened the window and leaned out.

The night was dark, and as silent as slumber. The lighted candle threw my huge shadow on the opposite wall. From time to time a flash of lightning blinded me.

I thought of the man whose early life was spent here and who filled half a century with the clamouring of his grief.

I thought of him first in these quiet streets, playing with the village boys and looking for nests in the church-steeple and in the woods. I imagined him in his little room, leaning his elbows on the table, and watching the rain beating on the windowpanes and the clouds passing above the curtain, while his dreams flew away. I thought of the bitter loneliness of youth, with its intoxications, its nausea, and its bursts of love that sicken the heart. Is it not here that our own grief was nourished, is this not the very Golgotha where the genius that fed us suffered its anguish?

Nothing can express the gestation of the mind or the thrills which future great works impart to those who carry them; but we love to see the spot where we know they were conceived and lived, as if it had retained something of the unknown ideal which once vibrated there.

His room! his room! his childhood's poor little room! It was here that he was tormented by vague phantoms which beckoned to him and clamoured for birth: Attala shaking the magnolias out of her hair in the soft breeze of Florida, Velléda running through the woods in the moonlight, Cymodocée protecting

Little by little the day dawned; the wick of the candle grew longer and longer and its flame slowly faded away. The roof of the market appeared in the distance and a cock crowed; the storm had passed; a few drops of water remained in the dust of the road and made large round spots on it. As I was very tired, I went back to bed and slept.

We felt very sad on leaving Combourg, and besides, the end of our journey was at hand. Soon this delightful trip which we had enjoyed for three months would be over. The return, like the leave-taking, produces an anticipated sadness, which gives one a proof of the insipid life we lead.